About the Author

I am an eighty-six-year-old widow, who decided to write the personal story of my paternal grandfather during the Covid 19 lockdown. I live in the Scottish Highlands, and enjoy regular visits from, and to, my large family, and also the occasional afternoon tea and glass of sherry!

Family Matters

Best Wishes!

Margaret

Margaret Martin

Family Matters

Olympia Publishers
London

www.olympiapublishers.com
OLYMPIA PAPERBACK EDITION

A CIP catalogue record for this title is
available from the British Library.

ISBN: 978-1-80074-435-6

This is a work of creative nonfiction. The events are portrayed to the
best of the author's memory. While all the stories in this book are
true, some names and identifying details have been changed to
protect the privacy of the people involved.

First Published in 2022

Olympia Publishers
Tallis House
2 Tallis Street
London
EC4Y 0AB

Printed in Great Britain

Dedication

I dedicate this book to the memory of Gene, my late husband, and to my much-loved children, grandchildren, and great-grandchildren.

Acknowledgements

I wish to thank my daughter, Debbie, for all of her help, and her husband, Andrew, for his research and typing. I would also like to thank all of my family members for their support and memories, which have given life to my grandfather's story.

Chapter One
Isaac

I woke up very early on June 13th, a Thursday in the year 1895. As I rubbed the sleep from my eyes, the reason for my early rise dawned on me; this was my big day, the day when my boyhood finally ended, and manhood beckoned. At last I was free to do exactly as I pleased, needing no one's permission. I washed and dressed very slowly, with unusual meticulous attention to my teeth and fingernails; I was seventeen years and two months old, and my own master. When I finally appeared in the kitchen, Kitty, our elderly maid of all work, gave me a kiss, a thing she had never done before, thank God, and ordered me to sit down at the table. She'd a wee surprise for me, she said, so I dutifully obeyed and closed my eyes as instructed. On being allowed to open them, I saw a small box tied with a narrow ribbon. "Open it," she ordered, and on doing so, I saw a funny little gnome with a tiny sprig of imitation heather in his cap. I must have looked gobsmacked, for she then explained that my "pixie", as she called him, would always bring me luck, and I must guard him well; if I lost him, misfortunes would come my way, and my happy future would turn sour. I promised I would treasure him, and was rewarded with a generous plate of bacon and two fried eggs, instead of my usual porridge. As I crossed the yard, I met Isaac, my elder brother, coming out of the converted barn, where our live-in servants stayed- we had three in total, and for once he wasn't whistling. "You're early," he said, managing a grin. "Big day, isn't it? Good luck, kiddo!" I smiled to myself, as I knew what he'd been up to; he was a great one for the girls, and we had a particularly pretty housemaid at that time, by the name of Nellie; maybe she'd given him the brush off, though that seemed unlikely- he was a handsome guy, very tall and strongly built, and girls fell at his feet: maybe I'd get lucky like him now that I was a free agent, for I too was tall and strong, and the fair sex were not averse to giving me a kiss and a cuddle after the local dances.

With a jaunty spring in my step, I walked the half mile to work for the last time, and was greeted by my fellow joiners with a hearty round of applause, "Well done, lad," said the foreman, "Now get changed and brushed up quick- we've an early start today." We had a huge funeral, a local bigwig having thrown off his mortal coil three days earlier; I got into my mourners' gear smartish, all in black, my face a picture of misery. Mr Satterly, our boss arrived, looked us all over, and said, "Right lads, here we go." The horses were all ready in the yard, well brushed and gleaming with black plumes on their harnesses, the hearse in position behind them, containing a magnificent coffin, finest oak, with brass handles. Clearly, no expense had been spared by the family of the deceased to give their patriarch a fine send-off. I thought with a smile that it would surely take more than a fine coffin, and plumed horses, to convince St Peter to allow its occupant through the Pearly Gates; he'd been notorious for years with his shady business practices, and my father had no time for him at all — nevertheless he'd be attending the wake, along with the rest of Newcastle-under-Lyme's business community.

I walked slowly behind the coffin, dressed all in black and looking mournful, but inwardly shouting for joy. My apprenticeship at the undertakers was over, and I was now a fully-fledged joiner. All those years of knocking coffins together and getting a clip round the ear if a nail was out of place had ended at last, and I was free to start my own life. Mr Satterly gave me my papers when we returned from the interment, telling me that I was a fine joiner and would go far in my profession. Then, just as I knew he would, he sacked me, telling me that I could get work anywhere. "All the best, lad!"

I went straight to the nearby pub, downed a half pint, and strutted home to tell my parents how great I was.

Unexpectedly, I bumped into Isaac in the yard. He looked like thunder, and I wondered why he wasn't at our foundry, as he usually was at this time of day. He'd managed it for a few years now, taking over from Dad when he retired. "What's up?" I enquired, not really interested, but willing to listen until I could give him my great news- liberty at last! "The old buggers have given me a choice," came the reply. "Give up Nellie or get struck off, disinherited- no money, no future in the firm, nowt!" I was lost for words, never expecting anything like this, for Isaac was their pride and joy, and I was totally dumbstruck. "They'll come round, they always do," I managed weakly. "You're their golden boy, and when they see that you're going to get married this time, and give them grandchildren, you'll be the apple of their eyes again."

"Not this time," came the reply. "Ma's got her back up good and proper, and the old man's keeping his mouth shut as usual. Go in and tell 'em your good news and soften them up a bit. I'll come in when I've calmed down."

I liked my brother, but if truth was told, I was a bit jealous of his easy ride: he swanned about at the foundry, while I worked damned hard at the undertakers for tuppence.

You could have cut the air with a knife when I went in with my good news. Dad managed a "Well done, lad."

But Ma glared, and said, "Thank God, we have one decent son."

"I'll start looking for work tomorrow, Mr Satterley says he'll give me a good reference."

At which Ma gave me a twisted smile, and said, "No need, Davy, you'll be managing the foundry soon; did that layabout not tell you at the back door?"

"Come on now, Mother, let's not be hasty! Isaac does a good job, you know that. He's a good manager, and Davy has no business experience." I could see, though, that Dad knew the battle was lost. He'd spent all his married life being walked over, as the foundry had been in Ma's family, not his. He'd merely managed it for a while after her father became unable to do the job himself due to illness. After her pa's death, Mother announced that they'd get married, and he would continue as manager. He'd accepted that situation, as he'd accepted all the slings and arrows of his existence, and she'd ruled the roost ever since. When Isaac was born, she was apparently over the moon, doting on the beautiful baby, and as he grew up, spoiling her golden boy rotten, never having any time for me because I was "thick", she said, not clever like Isaac. Old Kitty told me this a few years earlier, when I was moaning about having to do an apprenticeship at the funeral directors. "She'll rue the day she spoilt that boy!" she observed, and her wise words had clearly come true. "I couldn't manage the foundry, Ma, I haven't a clue, and anyway

14

I don't want an inside job here: I want to see a bit of life before I settle down, so I'm going to look for joinery jobs all over the Potteries. You'd best make it up with Isaac — Nellie's a nice girl and he loves her."

"Loves her my foot. He'll be playing around as soon as he's married, when the scales fall off his eyes. We are not, I repeat, *not* having that slut in the family, and that's that!" She folded her arms, like she always did, to show us that was the end of the matter, and Dad said, "Would you like a glass of whisky, lad, to toast your success?"

"Aye, Dad, that'd be grand." I could see that I was going up in their estimation by the minute, and I thought that a bit of cold shoulder treatment wouldn't do Isaac any harm. He'd always been one for the girls, and I couldn't see him changing, any more than Ma could, but I was shocked when Ma ordered Dad to get onto our lawyer, Old Smithson, and tell him to draw up a new will, making me the sole beneficiary, money, foundry, the lot! "Aw, come on, Ma, don't be so hasty, he'll be back in your good books by tomorrow." I was flabbergasted, as I'd never considered that I would take over from the golden boy, but Ma just smiled and said, "Drink your whisky, son."

No more was said and I went out to the stables, where I knew Isaac would be cooling off. My brother and I both loved the firm's horses, as they gave us the unconditional love we lacked at home. Sure enough, there he was, hunched up on a bale of hay, the picture of misery. "She says I'm to inherit the business, if you don't give up Nellie," I said, rather unkindly, as I could see how miserable he was. "You'll get over her, like you've done with other girls before. I suppose she's up the duff, but you can help her out like you usually do." I'd heard from the lads at the Undertakers that Isaac took care of his

15

girls, if he got them in trouble, and didn't leave them in the lurch, as other young gents did in Newcastle.

He surprised even me by saying, "I really love Nellie, Dave — I've never felt like this before, and I'll not let her down. I'm going to tell 'em that they can keep the bloody business for all I care; it's fast going downhill anyway, because the old bitch won't put the money up to invest in new machinery. I'll soon get a management job somewhere; everybody knows me and I can't see you sticking the foundry for long, with Ma breathing down your neck. She can't live forever, and then, if she really did leave everything to you, we could share the proceeds. I've always felt bad that you'd get nowt. What do you think of that for an idea?"

Once again, I was flabbergasted. I'd known all my life that I'd get nowt at the end of the day, except for a few bits and bobs, but I'd never really thought about it; it was just a fact of life. I'd never considered that Isaac thought it was unfair and would probably have shared it with me. I was lost for words, and finally stammered something about letting her cool down- we could maybe discuss it with her and the solicitor. "She's made her mind up Davy, she's not going to budge, and I'm not crawling to the old cow. Give my idea some thought, and then, if you're agreeable, we'll get everything legally drawn up- not through the firm's lawyers of course! If she heard about this, she'd leave the lot to the cats' home! I'll go in now and try one more time, and if that doesn't work, I'll be off!" He was perfectly calm now, the horses having worked their magic, and I stayed with them, contemplating the future. Isaac was right; I knew I couldn't work with my parents, not with Ma at least. All I wanted was to escape, see life and have a bit of freedom. The prospect of half the estate when they passed on was beyond my wildest dreams, though I couldn't really believe that Isaac would chuck his inheritance away. Ah well, time would tell, and the parents would carry on for another twenty or thirty years anyway.

True to his word, Isaac stuck to his guns, and insisted that he was going to make an honest woman of Nellie, whether they liked it or not. Despite Dad's attempts to change our mother's mind, he was duly disinherited, and left home immediately, taking as much of the petty cash as he thought he could get away with. We found out later, when the auditors came to make their yearly report, that he had also syphoned off a good deal of cash from the firm's assets, but of course, even Ma agreed that we couldn't prosecute, as that would only compound the firm's difficulties, as well as make our family a laughing stock. I saw that Mother and Isaac were made of the same stuff, determined to get their own way, and hoped that I took after them, and not after poor old Dad, who remained a doormat for the rest of his life, which as it turned out was not very long.

In theory, I managed the firm for a short while, but Mother, seeing that the business would soon go to the wall with my inexperience and disinterest, employed a proper manager to handle the day-to-day side of things. I could just meet important visitors and show them round, being as pleasant as possible. I kept my eye on the job adverts in the local papers, and fairly soon one came up that appealed to me — teaching joinery to young lads who lived in a nearby Penitentiary for Wayward Boys under eighteen. "Good God, Davy, you're dafter than I thought," was Mother's opinion of my choice.

"I'll probably not get the job, Ma," I replied. "After all, I've no experience of teaching anything."

"I should think a degree in lion taming would be a better qualification, lad," was Dad's opinion, and he wasn't far off the mark, as I soon found out. I duly applied, sending a copy of my joinery qualification and a reference from Mr Satterley, the undertaker. I was soon called for interview, the letter telling me that several other hopefuls were also in the running for this prestigious position. The day arrived, and off I went, dressed in my best. The penitentiary was only a few miles from our place, so I walked there, enjoying the fine weather, scenery and the feeling of hopeful expectation. When I was called in, I saw at once that the Panel of Worthies liked the look of me and didn't appear worried at all by my lack of experience in teaching young people. "That will come, lad," was their only comment. "What is needed here is a teacher who can handle himself, and keep these boys under control, meting out the discipline they so lack at home." I walked back tired but happy, feeling that the interview had gone well, and I was not disappointed, for a few days later I received a letter, congratulating me and giving me a starting date three weeks hence. I sent my letter of acceptance immediately, and began brushing up my joinery skills on bits of wood that Mr Satterley let me 'borrow' from the undertakers.

I kept in touch with Isaac, and met him several times at a hostelry we both knew in Newcastle, an unfashionable one not frequented by anybody who knew us. He looked tired and explained that he was shacking up at a friend's place, and Nellie was staying at her mum's until he could find a home for them. Her father disapproved of Isaac, and refused to come to the registry office wedding, which was only attended by Isaac and his friend, and Nellie and her mother. "I would have come," I said, and he laughed.

"I bet you would, kiddo, if only to annoy Mum!" The

pregnancy was going well though, and Nellie was blooming. A few weeks later, he told me that he had bought a small house in a pleasant enough area, and he and Nellie were moving in the following week, just in time for the baby's arrival. He'd had no trouble getting a job managing a small foundry, and I smiled to myself as I thought of the 'deficit' he'd left us with — his new firm wouldn't have been quite so eager to employ him, had they known of our 'shortfall'. He laughed when I told him I'd got the job at the penitentiary, saying he could probably get me a shotgun cheap! Our talk always, it seemed inevitably, came round to the legacy I was to receive, and Isaac was quietly persuasive, never pushing the matter, but stressing that if we were to go ahead with the scheme, our arrangement would need to be legally drawn up, and that he would be willing to pay for that, as I had never worked, and consequently would be unable to pay my share.

After much consideration, I decided that it was probably a good idea. I didn't think I'd be able to save much from my wages at the boys' home, and I also knew that we'd be lucky to get much, if anything, for the business, which was now losing money hand over fist. I'd always looked up to Isaac, and thought that he had been very badly treated by our parents, considering he had made a good profit for the family for several years, and so I agreed to his plan. On the death of the last of our parents, I would be left with what money there was from the sale of the business, and Isaac and I would share the proceeds equally between us. We had a legal document drawn up by a firm of solicitors, who dealt with the business at his new firm, and all I had to do was to sign it, which I did on a visit to Newcastle, two days before I started my new job. Isaac and I drank to our happy arrangement, and he wished me the best of luck in my career as a teacher.

Chapter Two
The Boys' Home

The day finally arrived when I could throw off the shackles of childhood forever. I packed up my few possessions in a trunk, just a few clothes, a couple of books, and of course my lucky charm, which so far had done me proud. I said cheerio to our new manager and wished him luck, thinking he was going to need it, as the business was going downhill at a rate of knots. Isaac must have been a much better manager than we had given him credit for!

My trunk was hauled onto the back of one of our small carts by some of the foundry lads, Ma and Pa coming out to see me off. Pa wished me the best of luck, also saying that I was going to need it, but Ma just laughed, saying I'd be back in a week or two, once I'd seen what the real world was like. One of our drivers took up the reins, and I sat beside him, full of hope and expectation, but at the same time apprehensive of what my new job, and new life, would bring.

I was cordially received by a senior member of staff, and shown to my room, my trunk being manhandled up a flight of stairs by four of the lads. The room was sparsely, but adequately furnished, and I unpacked my few possessions very quickly, going downstairs as invited for a cup of tea. The beverage was the weakest I'd ever tasted, and accompanied by a solitary digestive biscuit, which, as I'd had no lunch, did little to satisfy my hunger pangs. My new associate, whose name was Ronald Clarke, was pleasant enough, and said he'd been given the job of showing me round. I thanked him, saying that I hoped I was not keeping him from his work, at which he laughed, and said that I was doing him a favour. We then walked round the place, and I saw classrooms and workshops, taking a particular interest in the joinery department. The boys were all working in the garden, as it was called, so I didn't meet them until supper time; they were a poor-looking bunch, and I couldn't help thinking that our meal of gruel, doughy bread, too many unsalted potatoes, and precious little meat, was not going to build them up much. When the so-called meal was finished, and the boys marched off to do their chores, Ronnie asked if I'd like to come with a few of the staff to the local pub, the Dog and Whistle, which served good ale and pork pies and the like. I politely declined, saying that I'd better prepare my lessons for the following day, as I'd no experience of teaching, and he smiled and told me I'd be fine, as long as I took no nonsense. "Good job you're a big lad," he chuckled.

After the next week or two, I realised that I'd had totally false expectations of my new job. I knew, of course, that Isaac and I had enjoyed a very different upbringing to the rest of the boys at our local school. For one thing, we were much taller and heavier than they were, warmly clothed in the winter, with lighter garments in the summertime, whereas the other boys wore the same things all year round. We always came out on top when we had fights in the playground, and believed we were better fighters than the others, but the reality was that our size meant that we would always win a fight, even though we were often outnumbered, just the two of us versus the rest. They were the children of our firm's employees, and yet poor as they were, they were still better clothed and fed than the boys in the home appeared to be. Newcastle was a town of two extremes, with very rich areas often sitting right next to slums. Our house, for instance, was a Tudor-style mansion, on a rise with gardens, a circular driveway for the horse and carriage to turn, and stabling for the firm's horses, as well as the family's. The foundry was half a mile down the road, belching out smoke and dust, and most of the locals worked for us. We went to the local school, because Mother didn't approve of private, costly education, as she'd been to a boarding school and had hated it, a total waste of money, in her opinion. The undertakers was on the fringe of both of these local areas, and catered for both ends of the social spectrum. The penitentiary was out in the country, with wide open spaces and clean air, and thus a complete contrast to the city. It was this that had given me a totally wrong impression of what my job would entail, as I soon discovered that the boys here were from even poorer areas than our firm's children, who were mostly well cared for, as their fathers were in employment. The families the boys here came from were, in the main, totally dysfunctional, with drink and despair as the watchwords. This of course percolated through to me over the next few weeks and filled me with anguish — how could I have imagined that I could help these poor lads, who'd fallen foul of the law from an early age?

Being the new "boy" on the staff, I soon discovered that I'd been handed the wildest bunch of lads in the place, and they did their best to intimidate me, mocking my 'fancy' clothes, laughing and shouting across to each other when I was trying to explain something, mimicking my 'posh' accent, and generally making my life a misery. I soon came to the conclusion that teaching was not for me, and if it hadn't been for the amusement that my return home with my tail between my legs would give my mother, I would have packed my bags at the end of the first week. I decided, however, that since I couldn't leave immediately, I'd better try to get a grip on the lads, and forget how sorry I was for them and their rotten lives. I therefore adopted a sterner approach, bawling them out for any misbehaviour, and handing out a slap or two. I suppose that I could have reported them to the headmaster, but that would have resulted in them receiving six strokes of the birch, and I couldn't bring myself to do that; these lads had suffered enough misfortune in their short lives without me bringing more upon them.

The crunch came one afternoon, when one of the lads pulled a knife on me. He had stolen it from the kitchen when the boys were washing up, cleaning the cookers and mopping the floor. I'd noticed that they did all the cleaning and heavy work at the home, and I assumed that the governors collected the wages of "employees" who only existed on the books. This lad, or 'Dog' as he was affectionally known, short for 'Mad Dog', came at me, brandishing this stolen knife. He was cheered on by the rest of the lads, all baying for my blood, but fortunately I was much taller than him, and probably twice his weight, so I easily overpowered him and relieved him of the knife, which I then held at his throat, saying that if he made one false move, it would be his last. I would plead self-defence, for which I'd be commended. To my surprise, he started to cry and beg for mercy, and far from rushing to his defence, the other lads cheered, all shouting he was 'crackers', and that he should be reported to the headmaster. I told them all, 'Dog' included, that I would not report the incident, but if anything like it occurred again, then I would not hesitate to report the matter. This solution met with their approval, and after that, I was respected and well-liked by all my boys, 'Dog' included. It amused me that I was congratulated by the rest of the staff, most of whom had been intimidated at one time or other, lamely calling on the headmaster and his birch rod.

I enjoyed teaching the lads joinery, and encouraged them to work hard, by telling them how they could get good jobs once they'd served their time and kept themselves out of trouble. They were generally a cheery bunch, despite the conditions and privations they suffered. They seemed to feel the cold worse than I did, and on going into their cloakroom, where they changed into their running gear, I noticed that they had no vests, despite the home's total lack of heating and its situation on an open moor, in the teeth of the gales that blew all year long, but especially hard in the winter. I decided that if I were to keep my self-respect, I had to abandon my own vests as well, and never wore one again for the rest of my life — a small gesture, but somehow it made me feel better.

The only relief from the privations of the home were the regular visits to the pub in the nearby village. We had a two-mile tramp to get there, usually battling icy winds, and then another two-mile tramp to get back to the home. These marches were worth the effort, however, as the beer and whisky kept us warm, and the hot pies and mash and plum puddings filled our bellies. The regular crowd was always the same, mostly colliers from the nearby pit, and we always had a good laugh with them, though they had as little to laugh about as we did. Over time, I got to know one of the colliers quite well, regularly playing cribbage with him, both of us bemoaning our lot. I entertained him with tales of the boys' escapades, and he told me of the 'joys' of labouring underground for a "pittance." He was a nice chap by the name of Charles Cooke, and I discovered that he lived with his parents and sister. He regularly asked me over for supper with them, never eating at the pub himself, but just downing a couple of pints to "wash away the coal dust," as he put it. He said his ma's grub wasn't up to much, but it was a damn sight better than the food I got at the home. I refused at first, knowing that their money was tighter than mine, but finally gave in after a particularly vile evening meal at the home. I was made very welcome, his mother fussing over me, making sure I ate my fills. His dad didn't say much, puffing on his pipe and coughing a lot. "He should'na be smoking with the state his lungs are in, but it's the only pleasure he has," Charlie told me later. His father had been forced to retire early due to emphysema, and spent most of his time in his chair by the fire. He received a pension, "Just a pittance," Charlie said, "but at least it pays for his baccy." I learned that my new friend was courting a local girl, Annie, a parlourmaid at a posh estate house nearby. He was trying to save up, so that they could get married, but it was getting harder all the time, as the seams of coal at the local pit were running out, and the wages with them. Charlie explained that he'd have to leave home soon to get more money, but he didn't want to leave Annie, or the old folk for that matter. My visits became more and more frequent, and I insisted on paying for them, rather more than I would have paid for the pies at the pub. I told myself it was to help Charlie's family, but really the main attraction was his good-looking sister Emily, who worked in the nearby estate office. I longed to ask her out, but hadn't the funds, or the transport, to take her anywhere nice, and I was certainly not going to ask

25

Ma for a 'sub', or she'd be saying come back home, and you can have all you want, though I didn't expect she'd be much impressed by me falling for a collier's sister.

Almost a year to the day after I left home, my father died of a stroke. I was very shocked by his sudden death, as I'd only been home once or twice since I'd started at the penitentiary, and he seemed fine on those occasions, congratulating me on sticking it out. "Say what you like, Davy, you're doing a good job for those poor lads. I never thought you'd last this long there, as I'd heard what a badly run place it was, with too many sticky fingers in the pie. If you can turn just one poor lad's life around, then your time will have been well spent, and I take my hat off to you, son." Ma just grunted and threw him a despairing glance, and surprised as I was by his death, I was even more shocked by Ma's reaction to it. I'd expected little in the way of heartbreak, but she was genuinely devastated, and I heard her sobbing every night in their bedroom. I took a fortnight off, without pay, to help her out with the funeral and business, and suggested that we should ask Isaac back for a few days to help out on the business side, but she said no — she had ruined Isaac because he reminded her of Dad when she married him.

"He was such a catch, you know," she said, smiling through her tears. "Your father was the most handsome young blade in the district, and he chose me. People think he only married me to get the business, but he wasn't interested in that — he wanted me for myself, and we had a blissful few years before his eyes began to wander again, and I had to take up the reins or the business would have floundered. No, leave Isaac be- he'll come if he wants to!"

The funeral was a fine affair, Mr Satterly doing the

honours as usual for the business community. Isaac attended and came to the wake, but stayed only briefly, offering Mother his condolences. If he'd expected a warm welcome back into the fold, he certainly didn't get it. I stayed a few days longer, and Ma told me that things were going badly at the foundry: she believed that the new manager was cheating her, dipping his fingers into the profits, but she couldn't prove anything. She almost begged me to come home, but I explained to her, in as kindly a way as I could manage, that I had no interest in the business. She really should get Isaac back, with his little family. I was sure that he'd be really pleased to be asked. "And have that bitch lording it over me? Never!" was the reply.

I returned to the penitentiary, but only eight months later came home for another sad occasion, my mother's funeral. She had died of a heart attack, having never gotten over my father's sudden demise, asking me to come home in all her letters. I felt guilty at not having returned to help her out, but told myself that she'd brought all her troubles onto herself, by her obstinacy over Isaac and his girl, now of course, his loving wife, and the picture of respectability. When Mother had been laid to rest beside Dad, Isaac and I left to have a drink and a chat, and I could see that he was very happy. He'd now got a better job, managing a larger foundry in Newcastle, and he and Helen, as she now preferred to be called, were very happy with their little son John, and another child on the way. He said they'd like me to come over for a weekend and return to being a family again. He didn't mention our inheritance, but I knew he was thinking about it: all the money and assets would come to me, and then be shared equally with him. Having signed the legal agreement, I knew he'd be keen to speed things up, but I was not so sure now that it was such a good idea. The money was much less than we'd anticipated, and only half of it was no longer quite so appealing, especially as I really fancied Emily Cooke. Charlie said that she fancied me as well and wondered why I didn't make a move. We arranged my visit for two weeks later, and I wondered how I could wriggle out of our agreement without irrevocably losing touch with my brother, whom I had already missed a great deal after his departure from the firm.

The visit went well at first, as I was made most welcome, with a fine dinner cooked by Helen herself. She appeared devoted to Isaac and the baby, a bright little fellow who was happy to play with me, throwing his toys for me to pick up. On the second, and final day of my stay however, things began to feel strained, and after a fine breakfast, Isaac suggested that his wife should take little Johnnie upstairs and the pair of them have a nap. "She tires very quickly, as she's so much to do, keeping house and looking after Johnnie. I don't think she'll be strong enough to manage all that and cope with a newborn as well," he explained when she'd left the room. "How about a glass of whisky before you set off back to the home?" I readily accepted, and we chatted for a while about old times and Mother's commandeering ways, and I told him that she'd cried her eyes out when Dad died, saying that he'd been the love of her life — she'd only taken over the running of the business when Dad had gone back to his philandering ways. Isaac laughed, saying that he'd heard rumours about Dad and his escapades, but hadn't really believed them. "They must be true, if you got them from the horse's mouth, as it were. It just goes to show that you can never judge people by appearances. Dad told me that he'd tried to reason with Mother when she threw me out, but to no avail. I suppose, once he'd had his

28

flings, he just settled down to doing as he was told. I'm amazed that they've passed away so soon — I thought they'd be good for another twenty years or so, but it's an ill wind that blows nobody any good, and at least it means that we'll get our inheritance all the sooner. What do you intend to do with your share?"

I replied that I intended to leave the home fairly soon, and told him that I'd hated it at first, but had now settled in to the routine and enjoyed teaching the poor lads' joinery, hoping that it would get them decent jobs in the future. "I just don't see it as being my future though. What about your future plans?" I enquired.

"Oh, my share's spoken for Davy. You can see that this house is rather small, and another child will make it feel even smaller; we'll have to employ a nanny for starters, as Helen can barely cope with one baby, and especially now that there's another on the way. We'll get a bigger place, and you'll be able to offer this girl Emily a bright future. Did you say she was your pal's sister? You'll have to bring the pair of them over for a visit next time and we can get to know each other. I could probably get you a decent job round here, as I'm well in with the business community, your pal Charlie as well if he wanted it, not in mining of course, but I can't imagine he'd be sorry to give that up!"

"Oh, I'm not sure I'm ready for a move over here, Isaac. Where would I live for starters?" He laughed, and said I'd always been slow on the uptake. "I'd let you and Emily have this place cheap, it'd do you for starters like it's done us, and your pal Charlie could have a room here, if I fixed him up with the right job." I stalled, saying that I'd not yet decided on my future career, and needed a little time to consider my options.

We parted amicably enough, but I think we both knew that the old brotherly times were a thing of the past. I was to sell the business, and then we would share the proceeds; what I did after that was up to me, Isaac said.

I went to the Cookes' cottage the following week for supper and a laugh, having almost decided to take up my brother's suggestion of getting a job near him, and buying his house on the cheap with my inheritance. The idea had its merits, but I didn't really fancy a job as a joiner, even as a promoted one, or as anything else in the business world for that matter. I yearned for a bit of excitement, a job that would keep me on my toes, and happy to get up every morning; a workday routine was not for me, if I could help it. Charlie asked how Ma's funeral had gone, and we downed a few beers, and I told him about my arrangement with Isaac that we would share the inheritance. "He's offered to get me a good job over there and sell me their house cheap- it's a generous offer and I know he means well, but I'm not ready for a routine sort of existence. I want something that'll get me up smiling, with something different to look forward to every day. Trouble is, I can't think of anything like that which will also pay the bills." We'd had a good meal as usual, cooked by Charlie's mother, and it was getting time for my departure back to the home, when Charlie suddenly said, "I've an idea, Davy. Your folk left you the money, not Isaac, he had his chance and he blew it. Why should you go against your folks' wishes and give him half? That's a daft idea! You should start your own business with your qualifications and your inheritance, and soon have enough money to set up home with Emily. Give notice at the home, I know you've had enough of it, and start your own business, and propose to Emily! There are plenty of other lads sniffing around, and she won't wait forever, and she certainly won't marry you while you're still at the home — she's heard enough about it to know that she couldn't bear living there."

I left Charlie's with my head in a whirl — I knew that I would love to have my own business, but I couldn't think of anything that I could start up with only half the inheritance. If the foundry had not gone downhill, it might have been possible, but I knew we'd be lucky to get much for the old place, even with the house included. The house itself was fine, but who'd want to live with a failing foundry in the vicinity? I thought long and hard about this over the next week or so, and finally came to a decision. I would keep all the money, as Charlie had suggested, for after all, Isaac would not have shared the money with me if he'd inherited it, as he'd expected. I could then decide on a career and propose to Emily, and together we would start a new life. I wrote asking my brother to meet me at the boys' home, and he replied, giving me a time and date. When we met, I informed him, over a cup of weak tea, that I intended to keep all of the inheritance, as our parents' will indicated, and that I would set up a business of my own. It would be much cheaper to start up out here in the wilds than in the big city of Newcastle. Predictably, he was furious, saying that we had a legally binding agreement, and that he would sue me if I didn't stick to it. With a bravado that I didn't feel, I told him to go ahead: I would say that he had forced me to sign under duress; our family name would be dragged through the mud, and even if he won the case, his legal fees would be astronomic. That meeting was the last time Isaac and I ever met! I loved my brother, but I loved Emily and my own future prospects even more. I sold the family business for the best price I could get, and proceeded to buy a pub in

Cranberry! The Red Lion was a decrepit-looking establishment, but something drew me to it; I felt that I had seen it before, but was sure that this was impossible. However, I told Charlie of my feeling and he checked with his parents. His dad remembered that many years ago, the place had been managed by an old couple by the name of Brindley, who'd had a son who had gone to college somewhere and married well in Newcastle — he was a manager at a foundry, as he recalled. Then the penny dropped — the son in question was my own father, and he must have taken us to visit his parents, from time to time. I wished that I could check with Isaac, as he would have more memories of the place, being that much older than me, but I couldn't bring myself to contact him, and have him laugh at me for wasting our legacy on an old dump.

Chapter 3
The Red Lion, Cranberry

I secured the Red Lion for a good price, as it had been shut for nearly two years, its business having petered out, along with the coal in Charlie's pit. Everybody thought that I was a fool to buy it, even for peanuts, as it was a rather unprepossessing building, just a row of four farm cottages knocked into one building. It was even closer to the Cookes' place than the Dog and Whistle, so I worked at my new pub all day, using my joinery skills to do the place up, and then gave everywhere a coat of paint, inside and out. Though I say it myself, it looked grand, once I'd finished the improvements. I slept there every night on a wee truckle bed I'd got cheap, with bedding provided by Charlie's mum, who said it was surplus to requirements now that Aggie had left, Aggie being the eldest of the Cookes' children. "And the brightest," said her proud mum. She'd won a scholarship, and gone somewhere in the Midlands to train as a teacher, and now taught at a school down there. "Not like Charlie here- he took himself out of school when he was nine and sold firewood round the doors with a little donkey and cart."

"I was trying to help out Mum, you know that. When Dad took ill, we needed every penny we could get."

"I know, son, and I appreciated it, but I wish you'd stayed at school all the same. You were a clever wee laddie, and now you've missed your chance. Ah well, that's life, I suppose. Emily will up and marry soon, I expect, and then you'll leave as well with Annie, and your father and me will be left to a lonely old age." Charlie laughed, saying that this was Ma playing the old fiddle again, and we sat down to supper. I ate with them every evening while I was working on my pub, and then returned to my uncomfortable bed at the Red Lion, my "lunchbox" for the next day in my rucksack. I insisted on paying for my food, despite Ma's protestations, for I knew this was doing them a bit of good, in return for their hospitality. I was also seeing a lot more of Emily, and we were soon on kiss and cuddle terms. Life was good; my little charm was working overtime!

Opening night finally came, much to my relief, as my inheritance was fast running out. I opened the door at six thirty p.m. to a large crowd, mostly colliers from the nearby pit, Charlie amongst them. They'd all come to see what the old place was like, now that it had been done up. I shouted over the din that the first pints were on the house, and Emily ran about taking the lads their free beers. I'd made an arrangement with the same pie shop that the Dog and Whistle patronised, to pay them a farthing more per pie than the other pub did, in return for a little more meat in the pies, and my clientele pronounced them, "Top class!" The two of us were kept on our toes until closing time, and when the last group of colliers had gone, we gratefully collapsed onto the pub benches, with a pint for me and a half for Emily. We finally got to bed, my little truckle bed, at two o'clock, with our future all planned out. Emily accepted my proposal of marriage, and I was the happiest and proudest man in the world. I had the wife of my dreams, and a job I thoroughly enjoyed. My little pixie had come good again! Emily and I married three months later, with Charlie as best man, and his Annie as bridesmaid. The old Cookes were delighted, and we held our reception in the pub, my pub, with dancing to a local band. Charlie and I were now brothers-in-law, and brothers-in-arms!

I took to my new life like a duck to water. I was as proud as punch to see my name above the Red Lion's doorway, and quickly earned the friendship and patronage of the locals. My height and weight deterred any possible troublemakers, and life was rosy. I felt like the Squires of the past must have felt, looking over their domains, monarchs of all they surveyed. They say that all good things come in threes, and shortly after Emily and I tied the knot, the Cookes heard from Aggie that she had married her beau Fred, a bank manager no less. Aggie explained that they had married quietly in a registry office, with just two friends present as witnesses. They were moving to a bank in Manchester, as Fred had been promoted, and felt that they should conserve their savings to put towards a down payment on a house. The bank would help them with a low-rate mortgage, and as a manager, he would need a respectable address. "Typical," Charlie snorted, "He's a stuck-up beggar, that one! I don't know what's come over our Aggie, marrying a bloke like that. If that's what education does for you, then I'm glad I didn't have much!"

"Shut up, Charlie," his mother snorted back. "Our Aggie's done well for herself, and you're just jealous!" Charlie was by now actively looking for another pit, and applied for work in Moston, a colliery on the outskirts of Manchester. He got the job, and I learnt that the reason he'd applied for a place so far away from home, was that a house would be provided at a low rent in a nearby village, Failsworth. He married Annie a month later, a quiet affair, with only his mum and dad, and Emily and I in attendance. We gave money as our present to help with the move, and shortly after, they upped sticks and left for Failsworth. Their new house was only fifteen minutes away from the colliery by bike, and Charlie treated himself to one with some of the money we'd given as our present. We had a last drink together, Charlie and I, in my pub, and swore undying friendship!

Emily fell pregnant almost immediately, and produced a baby girl, a real beauty, whom we named Sarah Alice. The birth went well, mother and baby doing fine, and I felt that my brave decision to enter the licensed trade had been the right one.

The reputation of the Red Lion began to spread, with good ale, good food, and frequent dancing to the local band who'd played at our wedding. Workers on the local estates came in to see what folk were talking about, and immediately warmed to the friendly atmosphere. It wasn't just a drinking place, but also a place where you could eat and meet friends and enjoy a good pint at the same time. I soon found out that I could make a good living as a publican, and as the Red Lion's popularity increased, so did mine. I began to receive invitations to join in the local pastimes, which included shooting, fishing, poaching and the like. A wee bung to the local gamekeepers ensured that my new poaching friends and I were never caught and prosecuted. Emily worried that my new pals and I would be apprehended, and probably imprisoned, but she soon calmed down and enjoyed the new life as much as I did. We could soon afford a nursemaid to help with the baby, Sally, as we called her for short, so she could get out and about, taking tea with our new friends, gamekeepers' wives and the like. We were not yet part of "the gentry", but were getting closer all the time.

Emily needed transport for her socialising, so we bought a pony and trap, and I taught her how to drive it. Tommy, the pony, was a bit of a character, but very gentle, and I loved to go in the stable when I had a minute to have a chat with him, taking a few carrots, which he loved. It brought back happy memories of life at home, when Isaac and I would slink off to the stables and the good company of the firm's horses. I still missed Isaac very much, his dirty jokes and tales of his conquests, but I couldn't bring myself to go and see him and apologise. Eating humble pie was never to my taste!

When we'd enjoyed our first twelve months in the pub, it began to occur to me that we were missing a great opportunity to make some real money, more than I'd ever dreamed of when I became the licensee. The Newcastle gentry, as they liked to think of themselves, enjoyed outings to the country in their horse and traps. My parents had made many such a trip, much enjoyed, though Mother had always complained that the trip would have been much more pleasurable if they could have had a cup of tea and a cake before returning home, the only stopping places being dirty old pubs full of even dirtier old clientele. "We have to stop somewhere, Mother, to rest the horse. We could take a picnic, you know."

"Oh yes," Mother would reply, "and who would make it? Not the maids or Cookie, they've enough to do, and I don't suppose you'd offer your services! It would fall to me, as if I don't have enough to do, what with running the factory and keeping an eye on Isaac and his girls!" I could quite see that my parents would not be alone in their enjoyment of the drives out of the city, the gentry liking to escape from the filth and grime that their businesses created. Cranberry was about ten miles out of Newcastle, the perfect distance for a horse and trap, and I was sure that, if there was something at the end of that drive to attract them, they would flock to the pub once the word got around. Emily agreed, and favoured a sandwich and slice of fruit cake, with a cup of tea, but I thought the men would prefer something more substantial, and the longer they stayed at the pub, the greater the takings would be from the liquor sales, which of course would be the real money maker! We finally settled on ham and egg "teas," with a slice of fruit cake to follow. "What about the horses?" Emily queried. "They can't just stand around for that length of time!"

"No indeed," I replied, having thought of what I hoped was everything before I raised the matter. "You know the old barn at the back? Well, we could do it up a bit, the roof especially, for it was always raining. The horses could then be taken out of their harnesses and led into the barn, where they'd be rubbed down and given a nosebag of oats. That would keep them happy for an hour or two!"

"All well and good," Emily laughed, "but who is going to do all this? I suppose I'll be cooking and you serving. What about the horses?" I then played my trump card; there were several local lads hanging about the place most days when they weren't poaching. For them, this was a dangerous pastime, as they didn't enjoy the perks that I and my new friends did. I would approach the smartest, by whom I meant the cleanest, and enquire if they wanted regular employment looking after the gentry's horses, when the latter came to the pub for a drink and a meal. They jumped at the idea, promising me that they'd smarten up a bit, and make a good job of rubbing down the horses and feeding them. They'd all had experience of farm work, but the pay was lousy, and the work much heavier than just looking after a few nags! I then asked if they'd be interested in doing up the old barn at the back of the pub, paying particular attention to the roof, and this too appealed to them, same pay as for tending the horses, and starting Monday of the following week. We raised a pint of ale to our deal, and I congratulated myself on a job well done!

We already had a few hens, and I got a few more from a local farmer. He also obliged me with two sows. I got them cheap, in return for a few free pints in the pub, and they were both expecting happy events, so I felt that the ham and egg teas were well taken care of, along with the horses. We were now almost ready to unveil our new enterprise, and Emily thought we should place advertisements in a Newcastle paper. I felt, however, that we'd laid out enough money already. "Word of mouth is the best advert," I told her. "They'll all be boasting about their new find, once they've been here for the first time." "I'd better practise churning out the ham and eggs then," Emily said, but I surprised her, as I knew I would. "Nay lass, we need a pretty waitress, and I'm not fit for that job. You put on a nice dress and pinny, and I'll have a go at the ham and eggs. I watched our old maid Kitty make 'em enough times, and if she could do it, then so can I!" We went over to see the Cookes, as we often did, since they were on their own now that all their children had flown the nest, and I asked Ma Cooke if she'd make us fruit cakes. She was a great baker, and I knew the money would be more than welcome. We would provide the ingredients and pay her for the baking. She was delighted, the more so as she knew that we'd have to visit regularly to pick up the cakes. She and Dad were missing their family, and the landlord had upped the rent on their cottage. "I fancy he wants us out," Ma sighed, "and God knows where we'll go." I had a few ideas on that, but I kept them to myself for the time being. Charlie and I exchanged the occasional letter, and he was doing all right at the mine, which was just as well, he said, as his family was increasing rapidly, first little Gertie, then Bessie, then young Charlie. He was delighted that we'd had a wee girl, but asked when the son and heir was to appear, "or are you too busy making money, lad?"

Opening day arrived, with the old barn painted and the roof watertight, ready for the expected horses- we all had our fingers crossed. We had several sacks of oats from my farmer friend, and plenty of eggs. He also obliged me with a side of ham, to start me off. Emily looked lovely in her best frock, and a new pinny that she'd purchased on one of her trips to Newcastle with her friends. She'd also bought a very large striped apron for me, as she said I needed it, to look the part of a chef.

We opened the doors at noon, but only the regulars came in for their half pints. One o'clock came and went, and by two o'clock we were starting to feel edgy, when suddenly the clatter of hooves broke the silence, and alerted us to put on our best smiles, and go out to greet our first new customers. They stepped down from their trap, helped by one of the lads, who bowed graciously to them, and proceeded to unharness their horse. We told them that he'd be taken good care of, rubbed down and fed with a nosebag of oats, while they could relax and enjoy a lunch of ham and eggs, with a wee drink to wash it down. Emily ushered them into the parlour, as we now called the snug, and took their orders for aperitifs, to clear the dust from their throats after the drive. I went into the kitchen and began my new job as chef, feeling anything but confident. I kept my lucky charm in my pocket, and told myself that I could do anything that old Kitty could do, and once again my little gnome did the trick, as the plates came back polished clean. Emily reported that our first clients pronounced the ham and eggs delicious, the best they'd ever tasted. They'd enjoyed a bottle of white wine with their meal, and were now looking forward to their slice of fruit cake, which I knew would go down well with some coffee.

I was just starting to clear up, thinking that my cooking was over for the day, when I heard the clatter of hooves once more. We had another customer, this time a man and his wife and daughter, and they chatted with our first clients, who regaled them with the high quality of the meal. "Especially the fruit cake!" laughed the old girl. I was well pleased with our first day as an eating establishment, and treated myself to a well-earned pint. The lads were complimented when the customers left, saying that their horses appeared well refreshed by the attention that they had received, and slipping a little something to their grateful carers. That really pleased me, as I knew a few tips would keep the lads on their toes. I told them later that if trade increased, I'd employ them for a few more hours a day, to look after the pigs and hens, and we drank a pint to that. A prosperous future beckoned us all.

The trade took off beyond our wildest dreams, the popularity of the ham and egg teas spreading far and wide, and I began to receive invitations to join shooting parties, given by the local gentry proper. I knew I was a fair shot, as Isaac had taught me well when I was a boy, and I found that I could easily hold my own with these people, whose ineptitude with a rifle surprised me, given the amount of practice they must have given themselves. The invitations multiplied, and Emily became concerned at the amount of time I took off from the ham and egg teas, leaving her to do the cooking. We took on a local girl to act as waitress, but she wasn't much good at it, plonking the plates down, and often getting the drinks orders wrong. Emily felt that our business was beginning to suffer, and I knew that I would soon have to rein myself in, but then a stroke of luck came our way.

Charlie and Emily's parents had been struggling to find the rent for their tied cottage, ever since Dad had been forced to retire early with his emphysema, and any shortfall had, so far, been covered by their children. Charlie, as I knew from his letters, was finding it increasingly difficult to come up with his share, as his little family was growing up fast, and needing more and more of his wages from the pit. Aggie wrote to her mum, saying that she couldn't contribute any longer, as she too had started a family and therefore could no longer teach, childcare costing more than they could spare. That just left us to help out, but this only embarrassed the old couple, which was one of the reasons that I'd come up with the idea of serving fruit cake at the pub, paying Ma to make it. The crunch came soon after, when their landlord, Dad's former employer, suggested that they seek new accommodation; after all, they should really have left their cottage when Dad could no longer work at the pit, due to his lung condition. The firm had been generous in allowing them to stay for so long! I chuckled at the mine owners' 'generosity', but was glad that the old folk had to leave, none the less, as it was the solution to my problem at home. Charlie and Annie had no room for the old folk in their mid-terraced house in Failsworth, and Aggie said that Fred thought that she had enough on her plate, what with a second baby on the way. We, however, had room in the pub, and a helping hand or two would come in handy. We put the idea to Ma and Pa, and the relief on their faces was a joy to see. "We thought it was the workhouse for us," Dad said.

Ma shushed him, saying, "Come on Dad, we knew the family wouldn't let it come to that. It'll be lovely to stay with you at the pub, as long as Dad keeps off the ale."

"Don't worry, Ma." I laughed. "I'll keep him so busy that he won't have the energy left to lift a glass!"

We borrowed a cart from my farmer friend, and brought the old folks and their meagre belongings over to the pub. The journey wasn't far, but I'd wondered how the old fellow would cope. I needn't have worried, though, as he seemed to brighten up with every turn of the wheels, and even tried to lift stuff down from the cart when we arrived. I shouted the lads out to help and got Dad inside in a chair by the fire, refreshed with a half pint from the bar. The boys now worked at the pub full time, looking after the pigs and hens and Tommy, our horse, as well as our customers' horses. They had spruced themselves up considerably for the latter job, changing their clothes at lunchtime, and impressing the clientele with their politeness, thus receiving good tips from most of the diners.

The old folk settled down quickly into their new life, becoming grandma and grandad to little Sally. Grandma doted on the child and let her have her own way all the time. "Ma was never like that when I was growing up," Emily laughed, "and Sally's becoming a right little madam. She won't do a thing Nanny or I say." I just laughed, as I too doted on my little Princess, as I called her. The biggest change, however, came with Grandad, who seemed to have a new lease of life. He gradually took over care of the pigs and chickens, and amazingly, Tommy as well! "Nothing heavy mind, Dad," I told him, "That's what I pay the lads for."

"I know, David, and I won't overtire myself, but I feel stronger than I've felt in a long time, and my breathing's much better." We put that down to the pub's situation, on higher ground than their old village, with a breeze usually blowing, but really, I thought that what was doing him good was the feeling of being useful again, no longer on the scrapheap. Things went so well that I could skive off to the occasional shoot, without feeling that I was letting Emily down. She cooked the ham and eggs to perfection, and we found a new girl to act as waitress. Grandma enjoyed teaching her how to serve at table, just as she had done herself as a girl in one of the big houses in the district.

I got myself a trained gun dog from one of my acquaintances, and was amazed at his talents. Togo, as he was called, loved going on shoots, and carried his bag himself when we were off for some sport. I marvelled at how I could leave his bag on the ground when I went off on a limb, and he would sit beside it, guarding it, whether there was anything in it or not. My dream of becoming a country squire was becoming a reality, in my mind at least.

Chapter 4
Changed Days

Everything in the garden was rosy, especially when, one afternoon, Emily returned from what I thought had been an outing with her friends. She was bursting to tell me her big news. She had been to see the doctor in Newcastle, and he had confirmed what she already knew — that she was pregnant again! We were all delighted, the Cookes especially. I got the feeling that they had thought that we wouldn't be having any more children, so that we could devote all of our energies to the pub. I was beginning to wonder myself, what with Sally turning three a few months earlier. "You'll have a baby to play with soon," we told her, expecting her to be as delighted as we were. "I don't want a baby," came the prompt reply, "I've got my dollies and Grandma to play with."

"Grandma will be helping with the baby as well," I pointed out, at which she pulled a face and ran off through the door to find her "pal," Grandad, who let her dig in the garden until she was as black as a chimney sweep. "Oh, don't worry," laughed Grandma, "she'll love the baby when it arrives, we'll let her dress it and help with its bath. She'll feel like a proper little mother!" The only thing spoiling our happiness was Emily's morning sickness, which seemed to come on at any time of day. "You're working too hard," I told her, "You shouldn't be helping in the kitchen with a baby on the way, the work's too heavy for you, lifting pots and pans. I'll stay home every day to do the cooking, and Ginny, as our new waitress was called, can do all the serving. She's picked it up really well with Grandma's training, and the two of us will manage fine. You put your feet up, you deserve a break." So it was that Emily rested on the couch most of the time, Grandma looked after Sally, I cooked, Ginny served the customers, and Grandad pottered about in his garden, as well as caring for the animals. Business continued to boom, and even the lads who looked after the customers' horses gave a hand, if an emergency arose. We were a good team, and I congratulated myself yet again on taking the plunge and becoming a pub landlord. Fortune has favoured the brave, I thought self-righteously.

Despite resting on the couch for most of the day, Emily was always exhausted, so different from her previous pregnancy, and I heaved a sigh of relief when she went into labour. Grandma took control, and I drove off in Tommy's little trap, to fetch the local midwife. She busied herself with Emily and I paced about, willing it to be all over soon. After what seemed to be an eternity, the midwife popped her head round the door, and told me to fetch the doctor — things were not quite as they should be. I raced off again in the trap, heart thumping, and our good doctor got up from his Sunday dinner and came at once. I can't describe the relief I felt when I heard a faint little cry from our bedroom, and the doctor came through to tell me that I had a bouncing baby boy.

"Nine and a half pounds," he said. "A big lad, like yourself!" The midwife came out of the bedroom carrying a bundle swathed in shawls, but I had no interest in that. All I wanted was to kiss my lovely wife, and then say a prayer, thanking God for his goodness.

The baby was a healthy specimen, bawling for his bottle most of the time. Emily was too weak to feed him, and had little or no milk, Grandma said, but not to worry; babies thrived on cows' milk, especially if you added a few crushed biscuits to it, of the cream cracker variety, and her theory proved correct, as the infant gained weight every time the midwife called in to check on him. She and Grandma got on like a house on fire, and often took a wee drop of sherry together, if the midwife had finished her rounds for the day.

Business at the pub continued to thrive, the customers enjoying the free drink to wet the baby's head, and the christening was arranged for a Sunday, three weeks after the birth. It was a happy occasion, with everyone wearing their Sunday best. Sally looked beautiful in a new frock, bought specially for the occasion. Most of the locals attended, all spruced up, including gamekeepers and minor gentry, my shooting companions. The only fly in the ointment was Emily's continuing indisposition, and I was grateful that we had Grandma to look after the children. Not for the first time, I thanked God that the old couple had come to live with us, knowing that we could never have managed without them. We christened our son Arthur, after no one in particular. I would have liked to call him Isaac, after my brother, and swithered about inviting him and Helen to the christening, but chickened out, assuming that he'd decline, if he bothered to reply at all. It had been six years and eight months since we parted company, and I felt that I had enough on my plate, without stirring up the quarrel with my brother again. Perhaps when Emily had recovered her strength, I would go over to his workplace and eat some humble pie. I could offer to pay him his share of the legacy in instalments, as we were doing so well, and invite him over with his wife and children to meet Emily and our two nippers. I liked this idea, longing to have his approval again. I think, only now, I was realising just how much I missed him and his advice, welcome or not.

Emily still spent most of her time lying down on the sofa; she was permanently tired, and the doctor prescribed a tonic to buck her up. Neither Charlie's family nor Aggie's had managed to get to the christening, Charlie through lack of the readies, and Aggie because Fred hadn't been able to take time off, and I felt that seeing her family all together again would have been the best tonic she could have had. Her friends called round regularly to visit her, and I tried to get her to visit them in return, as they constantly invited her, but to no avail. "I just don't have the energy, David, I don't know what's wrong with me." She would burst into tears after these discussions, and Grandma said, "Don't upset her, Davy, she'll come round with time." The tonic seemed to have no effect at all, and she began to complain of a constant pain "down below", as she put it. The doctor called again, but could not find any physical cause, and suggested that she was one of those women who suffered depression after a birth, particularly after a difficult one, as our baby's had been. "She'll get over it, David," he told me, "Just give her time." Grandma looked after the baby and encouraged Sally to help with his bath and feeds, but Sally had no interest in him whatsoever, saying he was smelly, and wouldn't do anything she told him, hardly surprising, as she constantly told him to get up and walk and play with her. She spent most of her time with Grandad Cooke as before, kissing her mother only when told to do so. She seemed to blame Emily for producing the baby and spoiling everything. Emily, for her part, rested all day long, and took no interest in the children, or in anything else for that matter.

To my shame, I began to weary with the constant atmosphere of doom and gloom. I worked hard every day cooking, and every evening serving in the bar, trying to maintain a jovial atmosphere, but I increasingly felt that my good times were over, and I was destined to live out a dreary existence of work, more work, and then even more work. I had to refuse all invitations to go shooting, and my sporty friends began to stay away from the pub in the evenings, as did some of the other regulars. I assumed they went back to the Dog and Whistle, where they could have a good laugh, without feeling that they were disturbing the invalid with their noise and jollity. I adored my beautiful, if wayward little Sally, but couldn't feel anything for Arthur, the interloper who had caused all our troubles. The less I saw of him the better, and our relationship remained strained and distant for many years. I thanked God again for Grandma and Grandad Cooke.

The doctor still came regularly to see how Emily was getting on, but told me constantly that he could find no physical reason for her tiredness, and for her lack of interest in the children. "She'd been such a good mother to Sally," he said, and it was all a mystery to him.

"And to all of us," I replied, "Are you sure nothing can be done?"

"I could get a specialist to come along and have a look at her," he said, "but of course that wouldn't come cheap."

"Don't worry about the cost," I replied, "I would gladly go bankrupt if necessary to get Emily back to her old self."

The specialist, a Mr MacPherson, duly arrived and gave Emily a thorough examination, and she put on a bit of a show for him, praying, like me, that he would be able to recommend something that would bring her back to normal. When we went outside, the surgeon, as I discovered he was, said he was sorry, but he had found nothing physically wrong with her. "I can only assume that she can't shake off a bad dose of post-natal depression, as your doctor has told you. There is one thing I can suggest, however, and that is a complete change of scenery. Would it be possible for your wife to take a holiday, preferably by the sea? The fresh sea breezes and new surroundings might lift her out of her lethargy. She would need someone responsible to go with her, and it would be better if the children went too. Could you manage that?"

"I would move heaven and earth, if that would make her feel better," I replied. Relief flooded over me, and I thanked him for his time and helpful advice. "What do I owe you, sir?" I asked.

To my surprise he laughed and said, "One of your famous ham and egg teas, and a pint of ale — your lads are looking after my horse, and I've no further appointments for today, so I might as well enjoy myself! Enjoyment is a great cure for the troubles of this life, as I pray your wife will discover." I shook his hand, fighting back the tears of relief at the thought that, at last, there was something I could do for Emily, and took him through to the Saloon, seating him at a corner table, and calling for a pint of ale. I then went into the kitchen and told Grandma that a whole fruit cake was to be wrapped up and given to the Surgeon. "I think we're on the right track at last, thanks to this chap — remember, no charge for anything he might ask for!" I had a feeling that he might appreciate coffee and a brandy after his meal, and I was not mistaken!

That evening, after we'd closed up for the night, the

Cookes and I sat around Emily's bed, and we all discussed the specialist's advice. Emily was looking happier than she had in ages, thankful that something could be done at last, and we all put forward ideas as to where would be the best place to go. Grandad scratched his head, as he always did when he was thinking, and came up with an idea that met with everyone's approval. "I went to Blackpool once, when I was a lad — it was a jolly place, and the sea breezes nearly blew you off your feet. How do you feel about that, lass?" Emily smiled, and replied that if it was good enough for her dad, it was good enough for her.

I lost no time in asking my more affluent associates if they knew anything about Blackpool, and one of the senior gamekeepers gave me an address near the South Pier, there being three great piers in Blackpool, with entertainments on them, and concerts and cafes, everything a holidaymaker might desire. He told me that there was also an enormous edifice called the Tower, which was full of amusements and cafes and dance halls, and a circus, with every wild animal known to man. "Sally will like that," Grandma laughed, "She's frightened of nowt — is there any sand to dig with her little spade?"

"Miles and miles of it," laughed Grandad, "Enough to keep her busy for twenty years or more!" I wrote off at once to the address I'd been given, and three weeks later we set off on our great adventure, Emily, Sally, baby Arthur, Grandma and myself, all dressed in our best and raring to go. Grandad was left in charge of the pub, with Ginny making the teas, recently trained by Grandma, and looking very pretty in Emily's fancy apron. Her sister was enlisted to serve at table, and Ginny rehearsed her very well, saying that a big smile covered any little mishaps. She was given another of Emily's pinnies, and one of the lads' sisters was brought in to give a hand in the kitchen with the dishes, pots and pans, and anything else that might arise. The lads themselves assured me that they would help with the clearing up after dinner and serve in the bar in the evening. "Don't worry, boss, we've got everything covered, and we'll bring in more help from the village if need be — just tell Grandad not to be too tight-fisted with the wages!" I felt confident that they would manage fine, as trade was not as brisk as it used to be, and I left a good supply of cash, so that the old fellow could pay the wages every week. I wanted to stay in Blackpool for as long as I could, to watch my Emily regain her strength and happy disposition. A local carter took us to Newcastle station, and we caught the train to Blackpool, full of hope and expectation.

Chapter 5
Blackpool

The journey passed quickly, as both children fell asleep with exhaustion from all the activity and excitement, and Grandma soon followed their example. Emily was wide awake, talking enthusiastically about the things we would be seeing and doing, and I was delighted by her happiness. We took a cab at Blackpool's huge station, and soon arrived at our lodgings, being welcomed by Mrs Barraclough, an elderly lady, who showed us to our ground floor Suite, as she called it. It was actually two large bedrooms with a bathroom in between, but the rooms were situated at the back of the imposing house, where it was quieter, Mrs B said, and could be closed off from the other rooms on the ground floor by locking a door into the corridor. The children couldn't wait to go out, so Grandma took them to the Front, as the promenade was called, a short walk from the house, and I got Emily settled in an armchair, and then unpacked everybody's luggage.

We were served a good dinner in the restaurant, as a room at the front of the house was called, and after a stroll on the prom, soon sank gratefully into our comfy beds. Emily was still wide awake and had loved the promenade, where I had pushed her in a wheelchair provided by Mrs B. We chatted late into the night, and I felt that at last a corner had been turned.

The following day, I enquired of our landlady if there were

any nursemaids available in the vicinity, to look after the children during the day, and was directed to an agency nearby, where I hired a pleasant young lass, Betty, and took her to our lodgings, or "digs" as they were called locally. Sally and Betty made friends at once, and even Arthur took to the young lady. Mrs B produced a large bassinet, and the three of them set off to play on the sands, armed with buckets and spades from Mrs B's inexhaustible cupboard. Emily was tired, but that was natural after the journey, so I took her to relax on a comfortable chaise longue in the parlour, with a tray of tea brought in by a maid. "You go for a stroll on the Prom," she said, "I'm fine here. Mum will be down in a minute, and we'll be happy to sit and chat — remember that lunch is served at one o'clock, love."

Everything about Mrs Barraclough's boarding house, or private hotel, as she called it, suited us fine. After lunch we all went out for a stroll, with Emily ensconced in the same comfortable wheelchair. The food and service were excellent, and I was sure that we had found the answer to our prayers at last. The days passed quickly by, with a visit to the Tower to go up in the huge lift, all the way to the top, which gave a view of the promenade, which appeared to stretch away into infinity in both directions. We visited the circus, which terrified Arthur, who cried every time the clowns appeared, much to Sally's annoyance. We even visited the huge ballroom, where Grandma danced with me, Sally and Betty, the nursemaid. She was like a young girl again, and I wished that Grandad could have seen her. Emily was delighted with everything and didn't feel at all left out of the fun, as I lifted her out of the wheelchair, wherever possible, and she soon felt confident enough to take my arm and stroll along the Prom, walking further every day. The piers fascinated us too, with their amusement arcades, where Grandma and Emily played roll-a-penny, winning lots of pennies, only to lose them all over again, before we left to take Sally on to the swing boats and roundabouts. Arthur was too young to go on the rides with her, but he enjoyed sitting in his pram, and clapping his hands every time she rode past us on her hobby horse. The childrens' favourite pastime by far, however, was playing on the magnificent stretches of sand with their buckets and spades, Sally and I making sand pies and castles, which Arthur promptly knocked down as he tottered about. "He can't help it," Betty explained to a furious Sally, "He's only just learned to walk!"

"Then he shouldn't walk about spoiling my castles — he should stay in his pram!" came the reply. "Let's go for a paddle," Grandma, the peacemaker would suggest, and she and Sally ran ahead to the waves, while Betty manfully pushed Arthur along in his bassinet, leaving Emily and I to canoodle on our deckchairs. It was almost like we were courting again. I stayed for a month, and then felt that it was time for me to return home to see how Grandad was faring. I was agreeably surprised to find that the pub had managed fine without my hand on the tiller. The workforce had done a great job, Ginny's teas going down well, and the new lassie, Nora, a big hit serving at tables.

She was a pretty little thing and had spruced herself up no end since I saw her last. I found I could share the cooking with Ginny and take the occasional day off to go on a shoot with my pals, taking Togo with his bag. He was delighted to be working again, as Grandad said that he'd been moping around since I'd left, never getting out to do his work. As for Grandad, he'd loved being in charge, and I got the feeling that he wished I'd stayed away in Blackpool. Once the word had got round that the Red Lion was a cheery place again, business had picked up rapidly, the locals all returning in the evening for their pies and pints. They were delighted to hear that Emily was enjoying herself, and our takings improved considerably, more than covering Mrs Barraclough's very reasonable bills. Grandma wheeled Emily along the prom every afternoon, and Emily herself was delighted with her progress, telling me in her letters that although she still tired easily, the niggling pain had disappeared, and the sea air had given her some colour in her cheeks again. Betty was an excellent nursemaid and peacemaker, and everything was going very well in my absence. I laughingly replied that I would have to get back to Blackpool, or goodness knows what she'd get up to! I took to going to Blackpool every other weekend, and then just once a month. The spring and summer weather was fine, and everybody was happy.

With no women in the house for much of the time, I decided that I'd better employ a housekeeper, as neither Emily's dad nor myself were much into housework, and the place was fast turning into a pigsty. I put the word around and had several applications, settling finally on a strong-looking girl, Beattie, who came from a neighbouring village, within walking distance of the pub.

After a week or two, when I'd seen how hard she worked, trying to sort things out, only to come back the next day to find the place a tip again, I suggested that she could move in, if she liked, and just go home for the weekends. She laughed, and joked that if she moved in, it would be full time, as she'd only come back to a midden on a Monday morning. I consulted

Grandad, and he thought that a woman in the house was a great idea! He really liked Beattie, who laughed and joked with him, flirting outrageously. I was glad Grandma remained in Blackpool, for if she'd come home, he'd have been in for a hell of a row. He was a completely different man from the one who'd never got out of his chair when I first met him. I had the lads give a wee box room a coat of paint, and told Beattie that she could move in there, if she liked. She could also go to Newcastle and choose curtain material and a rug, and a small chest of drawers for her clothes. We had Sally's bed going begging, there being no sign of my family wanting to return home just yet. She readily agreed and told me later that she and her mother rowed constantly. "Every bloody thing I do is wrong," she explained. "Ma should have had a saint for a daughter!" I soon found out that Beattie was indeed no saint, as she began to flirt with me, rather more explicitly than with Grandad. She made it perfectly clear that she was willing to provide other services if required, and I'm afraid that I soon succumbed to temptation. I had been celibate for what felt like an eternity, and there was still no sign of Emily wanting to come home. Grandad turned a blind eye, content to potter around looking after the animals, and the three of us settled into a comfortable routine. My visits to Blackpool became less frequent, explained by the difficulties endured travelling in the winter weather, and by pressure of work, now that trade had picked up at the pub.

On my next visit, I heard that Sally was becoming naughtier by the minute, and Grandma was struggling to keep her in check. "She's bored, now we can't go to the beach every day, as it's either pouring with rain or blowing a gale. She's fed up with colouring books and takes her frustration out on

Arthur — everything he does is wrong, poor mite. She needs to go to school, David!" I pondered this, but decided that school was too permanent a solution. I still prayed that Emily would suddenly decide to come home, though I'd no idea how I would have explained about Beattie! On my next visit, determined to sort something out, I was met at the front door by Mrs Barraclough, carrying a screaming Arthur. It appeared that Sally had hit him across the face with a little spade, and blood was pouring from the wound. Mrs B said that she was taking him into her kitchen to dress his injury, and she told me, rather curtly, that everything was getting too much for Grandma.

I tried to remonstrate with Sally, telling her that Arthur was still a baby, even though he could run about now. "I don't care," she replied. "I hate him, he spoils all my things. I want someone nice to play with!" I decided to ask Emily what we should do, hoping that she'd say that she wanted to come home. Her initial improvement on arriving in Blackpool seemed to have come to a halt, and she spent her days lying on the chaise longue in the parlour. There were very few other guests at the boarding house, now that it was winter, cold and very windy. "You could employ a tutor for her," came the immediate reply, and I got the feeling that Emily, Grandma and Mrs Barraclough had a battle plan ready for my visit. "A tutor!" I exclaimed. "She's far too young for that!"

"Not at all," Emily replied, "She's very bright and wants to learn new things."

"But she's not six yet, surely she'd prefer other children to come in to play!" That suggestion was immediately rejected. "We've tried that with a neighbour's family, but Sally said that they were stupid, almost as stupid as Arthur, and she threw a book at one of them, so they won't come again!" I began to get the message! "I don't suppose Mrs B knows of a good tutor around here for a five-year-old?" I enquired, as innocently as I could. "As a matter of fact, she does. One of her nephews has recently finished his course at Liverpool University; he's got his degree but can't find a job befitting his qualifications. She's sure he would take the task on, as he likes children, and is bored doing nothing."

"Then perhaps Sally and I should meet him," I said, "and see how they get along, and more importantly, what his charges would be."

"Much cheaper than sending her to a private school," came the reply, and I inwardly wept at the change that illness had brought to my dear Emily, who would never have dreamt about private education for our children — I couldn't help thinking that she hadn't even considered the possibility of coming home. The tutor came round the next day, summoned by his aunt. He was a pleasant enough lad, who looked as though he'd never done a day's work in his life, and probably hoped that he'd never have to. He and Sally got on like a house on fire, and when I enquired about his fees, he obviously had no idea what to say. He was to come five mornings a week, and he finally said that he would be happy with ten shillings, to which I replied that I could run to one pound, but no more. He was delighted, and I could see that he had only wanted beer and cigarette money, with possibly a little left over for girls.

We shook hands, and I asked him to start the very next day. I stayed for a few more days to see how the arrangement went on, and whether or not it would encourage any improvement in Sally's behaviour. Things could not have gone better; he seemed to have a good general knowledge, teaching

Sally reading, sums and writing, mixed with stories about far-away countries and historical figures. He was able to make up a syllabus overnight, and I was very impressed, as was Sally, who loved both her lessons and her tutor, calling him "Sir" as requested. Mrs B. was well pleased also and said that I was generosity itself. I got the impression that she considered her nephew a layabout, who would never get a proper job if he could avoid it, just as I had done, but now I was not sure. Sally's behaviour changed immediately, and she completed all of her "assignments", as the tutor called her homework, in the afternoons, as well as lessons in the morning, and so was tired out after tea and willing to go to bed early. Grandma gave little Arthur all of her attention, so that he couldn't disrupt the lessons or homework, and peace was restored. Emily showed little interest in Sally's progress, however, and either stayed in bed or lay on the chaise longue in the parlour.

Grandma told me, before I left, that the tutor was just what Sally needed to keep her wee brain busy. "She's a very clever girl, you know David, and poor Arthur stood no chance with her — she thinks he's stupid, but of course he's not, for his age. I'm going to give him plenty of attention now that her ladyship is fully occupied, and I think that wee Arthur will surprise us." I learned over the next few months that Grandma and Arthur drew pictures and coloured in drawings together, and she told him all of the fairy stories that she'd told her own family. He came on in leaps and bounds, and Grandma decided that he should be given a very important job on dry days. Down the street, a short distance from Mrs B's, was a large ice cream parlour, Pablos by name, and they sold ice cream in all colours and sizes. Sally had originally been given the job of fetching it for Mrs B's puddings, but after a day or two fell out with the assistant at the shop and threw the ice cream on the ground. She was never sent again, and Grandma decided that Arthur could be entrusted with the job, now that he was "a big boy". Every fine day, he walked all by himself, carrying a jug for the ice cream. He had to ask Pablo to fill the jug with whatever colour Mrs B required, and then very carefully carry it home, not spilling any on the pavement. "And remember to always say please and thank you," Grandma reminded him. He didn't know, of course, that Grandma watched him all the way there and all the way back; he carried the money for the ice cream in a little purse, which dangled round his neck, Pablo relieving him of it and giving him a big smile, and a dollop of ice cream in a dish while he waited for his jug to be filled. "He's never spilt a drop," Grandma told me. "And the people at Pablo's think he's wonderful — so happy and polite. You've a lovely son David, as well as a clever daughter. I pray every night that Emily will get better soon and see for herself what beautiful children she has." The old lady's eyes filled with tears, and I had a sinking feeling that things were actually getting worse for Emily, not better, as we'd all prayed.

Time went by, and when spring came, I hoped that Emily would pick up again, as she had done the spring before, when we had first come to Blackpool. She'd possibly go out for walks along the prom again in her wheelchair and take a trip to the mighty Tower. I'd spent Christmas at Mrs B's, and although we had a fine turkey with all the trimmings, Christmas pudding, well stuffed with threepenny bits, a large, gaudily decorated tree, carol singing by the fire and a large selection of wines and spirits, Emily took little interest in the proceedings. If anything, she was more withdrawn than ever. On a visit in March, when spring was firmly in the air, I pressed her as to what was troubling her, and she told me, reluctantly, that the niggling pain "down below" had returned, even worse than before. She burst into tears, and try as I would, I could not console her. Looking back, I think she knew then that something was very, very wrong, and was unlikely to improve. I tried to persuade myself that it was just severe depression, as the doctors had said, but I was more than ever sure that the problem had a more serious cause. Matters came to a head that April, when Grandma wrote me a letter, telling me that Emily was crying with pain in the nights, and wanted to come home. "She needs all her family around her, David," she wrote. "She's very, very sick, I fear, laddie!"

I made arrangements right away for her return, and left home for Blackpool with a heavy heart. Grandma had organised all the packing with Mrs Barraclough's help, and a carriage was booked to take us to the station the following day. Tearful goodbyes were said, and the tutor came over with a present for Sally, a magnificent encyclopaedia, which caused her to dry her tears for a little while as she examined it. I thanked Mrs B for everything she had done for us, promising to return in happier times, at which she too joined in the weeping, saying that she prayed every night that poor Emily might be relieved of her suffering.

We were a sombre group in our carriage, even the children sitting quietly. Sally clutched her encyclopaedia all the way home, never saying a word. I think we all knew that we would not be returning to Blackpool, at least not for a very long time.

Chapter 6
Family Visitors

We arrived home in the evening, with Emily completely exhausted. She went straight to bed, never noticing the welcome Beattie had organised for her — vases of flowers everywhere, the house immaculate, with bags of potpourri in every room, quite overpowering the usual smells of cooking, pigs, hens and horses. I had wondered how my housekeeping arrangements would go down with my wife, but I need not have worried. She was oblivious to everything, remaining in bed every day, being cared for by her mother. Beattie looked after the children, along with all her other jobs, and I made the ham and egg teas, helped by Ginny, with Nora serving the tables. Everything was essentially the same as before, but now totally different — it was as though a light had gone out in our lives. I engaged another specialist at once, but he too could offer no explanation of Emily's condition, other than depression. My beautiful, loving wife, reduced to this shadow of her former self!

I struggled to find a solution to our problems, anything that could ease the strain that we all felt, and finally came up with what I hoped was a good idea. Emily's brother, my old pal Charlie and his wife Annie, had settled into life at Failsworth, and now had three children of their own, Gertie, Charlie junior and Bessie. Charlie senior made enough at the

Pit to give them a pleasant, if fairly frugal existence, but of course there was nothing left over to cover pleasure trips, so I suggested, in one of my infrequent letters to him, that he bring his young family over to us for a summer holiday. They could stay at our place for as long as they liked, and he could go home to work on weekdays, just coming to us for the weekends. Charlie jumped at this idea, saying that a holiday in the country was the very thing to put some colour into the kids' cheeks. I knew that he didn't much care for "townie" life, as he called it, and missed his roots. He also missed seeing how his parents were getting on, not forgetting his poor sister Emily. I hoped that seeing them all again would do her some good as well. Charlie and his family duly appeared, arriving by train at Newcastle station, myself and Sally driving there to pick them up. Sally was very keen to learn to drive Tommy, but thought he was a racehorse, so I had to "rein her in," much to her annoyance. The family had a large trunk, so Tommy had to work hard on the return journey, plodding along wherever there was an incline. "He's a lazy old thing," she explained to the visitors, "I'd soon gee him up!"

I soon discovered the reason for the large trunk; as well as their meagre outfits, Annie had brought enough food to feed a regiment — homemade potato pies, apple tarts, homemade bread, you name it! "We didn't want to sponge on you," she explained. The food was taken to the kitchen, where Ginny nearly had a fit. "I know that your friend's name is Charles, but where the "Dickens" am I going to put it all?" she cried. Beattie laughed and said, "We'll serve the family what we can today and tomorrow, and then the pigs will enjoy what's left." I got my apron on, and took over the ham and eggs, while the girls sorted everything out. Beattie never failed to amaze me, taking everything in her stride as usual. The family soon got settled into the bedroom that they were all going to share, the parents in the double bed, and the nippers in three small trestle beds, which Beattie had borrowed from a family in her village, whose children had outgrown them. "Give them a quid or two for them," I told Beattie that night and she laughed, saying that they would think that Christmas had come early. The surgeon, Mr Macpherson and his wife paid us one of their frequent visits later that week — they regularly came for a ham and egg tea — and he thought that the visitors would certainly do Emily no harm, "but keep the youngsters away from her, they'd just tire her out!"

"Not a problem," I laughed. "They're outdoors every hour God sends, they only come in for their dinner and bed, as filthy as the miners in my brother-in-law's pit." Sally didn't have much time for them, and continued to study her encyclopaedia. I wondered if the tutor's parents had missed it yet, for I knew that it must be worth a pretty penny! Annie gave a hand with anything she could, but soon saw that she was in the way, and so spent most of her time with Emily. They had been good friends in the past, before they'd both married, and Annie tried to interest Emily in the good times they'd had, as when Emily had been chosen to be the May Queen, much to Annie's annoyance. She had got her own back by pinching Emily's boyfriend later that evening at the dance in the village hall! She reminded Emily of all the good times they'd shared, and Emily smiled wanly, her eyes closing from time to time; she didn't seem to have the energy or inclination to chat, and would drift into sleep, leaving Annie to sit beside her, holding her hand helplessly.

Charlie also tried to remind his sister of pranks they'd got up to as kids, but equally to no avail. "God knows what's wrong with her, Davy, she's a different person. Do you think another specialist might know a bit more about her illness?"

"I doubt it," I replied, "but I'll try anything!" Another fellow came, recommended by Mr Macpherson, who knew him to be a clever guy. They worked at the same hospital, though specialising in different areas — this chap specialised in brain disorders. He could offer no solutions, however, and said he would waive his fee, as he had nothing useful to offer. He gladly accepted a ham and egg tea, saying that he had heard about them from Mr Macpherson, and then he left, wishing us well, only sorry that he'd been unable to help.

Although Charlie and Annie's visits didn't appear to be making any impression on Emily, I began to wonder if big sister Aggie and her husband Fred could do any better — it would do no harm to invite them for a break, anyway. They promptly accepted the invitation, saying that they could come for two weeks, as Fred's annual leave was coming up. I'd got their address from Charlie as Grandma couldn't remember it. "I'm not much of a writer, and our Aggie's too busy with her teaching," she explained. Charlie just snorted, saying under his breath that Fred was a stuck-up so and so, if ever there was one.

They duly arrived, and considering that they were allegedly very rich, according to Charlie, they brought precious little with them, just a small box of chocolates, which Emily pushed aside, telling Beattie to give them to the children. The men behaved civilly enough to each other, however, and the youngsters got on fine, revelling in each other's company, happily running wild, with Beattie keeping a close eye on them.

Aggie suggested that she and Annie should go to Newcastle, to see if there was anything that might interest Emily, so I took them in Tommy's trap, and they came back with a few love stories and some cross-stitch embroidery. Annie told Charlie later that Aggie had forgotten her purse, so she paid for the gifts, Aggie promising to pay her share when they got back to the pub. "You'll be lucky," came Charlie's reply, and indeed, when I asked Annie later if she'd got her money back, she said no, but it didn't matter — they were saving a fortune staying with us. "So are Aggie and Fred," I thought to myself, but kept my mouth shut.

Unlike Charlie, Fred fancied himself as a country squire, and insisted that I take him out shooting, "when you have a minute." I obliged, rather unwillingly, as we were mad busy, and between us we winged a few birds, Togo retrieving them, and bringing them to us to be put out of their misery, then into his bag. I explained to my brother-in-law that Togo would guard the bag with his life. "He's the best dog that I've ever had," I explained, omitting the fact that he was the only gun dog that I'd ever had! Fred was unimpressed, feeling that the dog's teeth would damage the birds. His theory was put to the test the following week, the day before he and Aggie were due to leave, their fortnight having come to an end. He came along straight after breakfast, when I was cleaning the kitchen and assembling my ingredients for the teas, asking me if I would take him out for one last "shoot". "Sorry, Fred — no can do," I replied. "As well as the usual number who come in on a Saturday, I've got one of these new-fangled charabancs arriving at lunchtime. I hate them, because a great crowd arrives at once, and it's total chaos — we need two of us cooking and two of us serving, if we can run to it."

"Couldn't I go myself, Davy? I know how to get to that place we went to last week, and I'd just try my luck and then come back home, hopefully with tonight's supper!"

"Nay lad, they have to hang for a few days, but you can go with Togo, if you like — he'll take you to the spot and you can bag a few if you get lucky."

"Great," he replied, "Which gun shall I take?"

I took him out to where the guns were kept in a locked cupboard, and handed him one with some ammo. "Remember, Fred, never leave the bag unattended. Togo won't go with you, he'll stay with the bag. That's how the dogs are trained."

"I'll be fine," came the reply, "Now where's Togo?"

"He'll be with Grandad, they're great buddies, but he'll go with you when he sees the bag and the gun."

"That's good," he laughed, and went off to find Grandad. I saw the old fella later, and he laughed when he said the shooters had got away all right, adding, "That Fred really fancies himself, don't he? Our Ag must have her patience tried!" The day passed quickly, as the pub had never been busier. On the face of it, the charabancs were good for trade, as they brought so many customers, but I wondered how long this trade would last. The charabancs could go much further than a horse and trap, and the gentry would not have the chore of driving them — maybe the day would soon come when the folk would prefer to be driven to places further afield, bypassing Cranberry altogether.

When the last of the day's visitors had left, and we'd cleaned up, the dusk was closing in, and I was thankful to sit down in the shade with a beer and my pipe — we'd certainly turned over some money that day! Beattie came and sank down in her chair beside me, kicking off her shoes. "My feet are killing me, Davy. Get me a beer, love." I obliged, thinking that I'd never seen her so exhausted! We chatted away, well pleased with how the day had gone, our visitors all occupied with the children, or sitting with Emily to give Grandma the chance of a nap. A wee while later Grandad appeared, a worried expression on his face. "Come and have a beer, Dad," I called, but he declined, saying that he was doing the rounds, looking for Togo. "He's never come back; I can't find him anywhere — is Fred home?"

"Aye, Fred's been around for hours, had his dinner and everything — maybe Togo's gone for a wander, after a bitch or summat."

"He'd never miss his dinner, lad," the old boy replied, and warning bells began to ring. "Sit down here, Dad, and have a drink — it's no good working yourself up into a state — I'll go and find Fred and see if he knows owt."

"He's in the bar, regaling the regulars with his financial expertise," laughed Beattie. "Sit down Grandad, Davy's warmed the seat for you, and I'll get you a pint." Sure enough, Fred was holding court, surrounded by a bored-looking group of local lads. "Can I have a word, Fred?" I called, and he came over, the lads looking relieved to be shot of him. "Seen the dog, Fred? We can't find him anywhere."

"How should I know his whereabouts? Chasing bitches, most likely!"

"How did you get on with your shoot bag?"

"No luck, not a bloody bird in sight!"

"So where's the bag, then?"

"God knows, can I get back to my pint?"

"In a minute, first let me tell you where the bloody bag is — it's where you left Togo guarding it, like I told you he would

— did you leave it where we went last week?"

"Somewhere round there — I went looking for birds, but there wasn't a oner in the sky, so I came back here."

"Get back to your beer, Fred, before I floor you." I told Grandad later that how I managed to stop myself punching Fred, I'd never know. Tired out as I was, I set off into the dusk to find my dog, calling out "Togo!" but knowing that he wouldn't leave the bag, even if he heard my voice. Night fell, and it started to pour with rain, and it was the best part of three hours later that Togo, the bag and I returned home, all soaking wet. Grandad was still up, worried to death, and he dried and fed Togo, while I dried myself off and downed a couple of doubles. On hearing the sorry tale the following day, Charlie laughed, "Have you told our Aggie? I bet it'd give her a good laugh. She pays a heavy price for going up in the world, as Ma would say."

"Don't be too sympathetic, she was the one who chose him after all, Charlie!"

"She was getting desperate, twenty-seven years old and unmarried," he replied. "She thought that she was on the scrap heap — better to take a fool than have nobody at all!" These words came back to haunt me a few years later!

Over the next twelve months, Annie, Charlie and their kids, and Aggie and her brood, visited several times, trying to cheer Emily up, all to no avail. She sank deeper and deeper into her own dark world, and eventually reached the stage where she couldn't cope with company at all: even her mother couldn't get any response from her, and she didn't seem to recognise any of us. Fred never came back again after the incident with Togo, "pressure of work," explained Aggie, rather sheepishly. Emily's final few weeks passed either in agonising pain, or morphia-induced sleep, and her short life ended on the kitchen table, being operated on by a young fellow from the local cottage hospital. When he came through to the parlour to give me the terrible news, he was covered in blood, and soaked in sweat. "I'm very sorry, Mr Brindley, I did all that I could," he said, and then proceeded to collapse into an armchair, crying his eyes out. I got him a large glass of brandy, and he gradually calmed down, Beattie getting him into the bathroom and cleaning him up as best she could. She told me later that this was the first operation he'd ever performed, and he prayed that it would be his last: he would try to get a job standing in for the other doctors in the neighbourhood. Whatever happened, he could not face an operating table ever again. He accepted another brandy and then departed, shaking my hand weakly, saying that he would pray that night for Emily's soul to rest in peace.

I never talked about Emily's death, just telling Sally and Arthur that Mummy had gone to live with the angels in heaven, and that she was happy there, with no more pain. Beattie was a tower of strength as usual, comforting Grandma and Grandad Cooke, looking after the children and keeping the pub and teas going. I went for long walks with Togo, returning late in the evenings with nothing in Togo's bag. I bottled my misery up, which I knew only made it worse, but I didn't know what else to do — a grown man couldn't go about crying like a baby, except when I was alone with Togo, who sat beside me, asking no questions, just being a comforting presence in my hour of need.

Emily was given a fine send-off, organised by my old employer, Mr Satterley. All the locals from the surrounding area and many of the gentry attended, along with the Cookes and Aggie, Fred once again being too busy to take time off. Mr Macpherson, the surgeon who had attended Emily a few years before, came to her funeral to pay his respects, and I thanked him for attending. "I only wish that I could have helped your poor wife, David," he replied, "but I think we both knew that Emily was already on a downward spiral. There's so much that we don't know yet, David, but we're learning all the time, thank God!"

"I should have agreed to a post mortem, I suppose, Sir, as the young fellow who performed her final operation suggested, but I couldn't bear the thought of her lovely body being mutilated even further."

"Don't blame yourself, lad. We get plenty of cadavers to examine. You were right to let your wife rest in peace. I'll leave you now, and remember, all is not lost — you have two beautiful young children to bring up, in a way your wife would have done had she lived — that is what you can do to preserve her memory." We shook hands, and the surgeon left me to ponder. What would Emily have wanted for the children, had she recovered from her illness?

I received many condolence cards, expressing sympathy for Emily's untimely death, but the only one that really surprised and upset me was from Isaac. I hadn't realised that my brother knew where I lived, and I toyed with the idea of replying, as the card had Isaac's business address printed on it. How did Isaac know that Emily and I had married, let alone that she had suffered an early demise? I couldn't decide what to do, so eventually decided to do nothing; if Isaac wanted to make contact, he surely would, and I felt that I had enough to contend with, without worrying about my brother. I couldn't shake off my lethargy and depression following the loss of my dear wife, and became a shadow of my former self. Beattie kept everything going the best she could, and tried to jolly me along, but to no avail. Business at the pub gradually fell away, as the cheery atmosphere had gone again, and didn't look like ever coming back. After several months, I decided that I could never be happy at the Red Lion again, the place holding too many sad memories for me. I felt that I needed a change of scenery, and thought about starting a joinery and funeral business, but rejected the idea, as I felt such a business would hardly lighten my spirits. I looked about for another pub, far away from Cranberry, and eventually something came up that I felt fitted the bill — a large hostelry in Newcastle. The Vine was advertised by the brewery as needing a new landlord, and interested parties were given an address to which they could register their interest. I duly applied, after visiting the area of Newcastle where The Vine was located, not a district I'd ever had cause to visit before. The pub was in the middle of a slum area, where everyone lived cheek by jowl. I was dubious at first, thinking that my mother would turn in her grave, but quickly decided that this was as good a reason as any for taking the tenancy, if I could get it. I smiled to myself, for what seemed like the first time since Emily had passed away. I asked her advice in my prayers that night, and rather to my surprise, she urged, "Go for it, Davy — you always liked a challenge!" After two interviews I was offered the job, which I accepted immediately; I wanted it cut and dried before the family had a chance to talk me out of it. To my surprise, the Cookes, Beattie and even the kids all told me to go ahead, and I then realised that we'd all been suffering from the aftermath of Emily's death, and needed something to lift us out of the doldrums. "The Vine will certainly do that," I thought to myself, chuckling; I hadn't chuckled in a long time. "Newcastle, here we come!"

That evening, after supper, I broached the subject of The Vine again, admitting that I'd already taken the job there, before consulting them. "It's a pretty wild pub, in a very rough area," I explained, "but I can handle it, with your help!"

"What do you want me to do?" Grandad asked, with a serious expression on his face, "be your bouncer?" Once the laughter had subsided, I told the old couple that I needed them to help with the move, and with childcare afterwards. "You're both indispensable!" I told them, much to their delight. The only fly in the ointment was Beattie. I asked her later, once the old folk and the children had gone to bed, to come with us — she'd become one of the family, after all, I chuckled, pulling her to me, and planting a big kiss on her welcoming lips. Beattie kissed me in return and said that she would be very happy to come, but on one condition — she wanted to become Mrs David Brindley!

I was shocked at this suggestion. "After all," I pointed out, "Emily is barely cold in her grave."

"Yes, I understand that," came the reply, "but I'm fast getting to the age where I need security, David. At the very least, I'd want an engagement ring on my finger, and a date set for our wedding."

"Let's leave it for tonight, love, while I think it over." I played for time over the next couple of weeks, but finally Beattie told me that she'd had enough of the waiting game and needed an answer. "It's either marriage or nowt, Davy!" I tried to explain that I couldn't face getting married again so soon after losing Emily. "Surely you can understand that, love?"

"Oh yes, I could, if only you hadn't been more than happy

74

to sleep with me while Emily was still alive, and in the next bedroom to boot!" One word led to another, and I told her that I would go to Newcastle, with or without her. True to her word, Beattie left the next day, and I never saw her again! A year or so later, I heard from Charlie that Beattie had married an old boyfriend from her village; he'd played around when he was courting her then, but now she had him completely under her thumb, and was pregnant by him. I suddenly remembered Charlie's words about his sister, Aggie; "Better to have a fool, than have nobody at all." Had I been the old fool that Beattie was prepared to settle for? The thought rattled me, and was to influence many of my later actions.

Chapter 7
The Vine — Newcastle 1912

The move, when it came, was far from easy. I regretted losing Beattie's organising skills on a daily basis. Not only did we need to transfer Grandma's and Grandad's belongings, which they had brought with them when they had left their cottage, but I had my parents' fine furniture to move — heavy, hard to manoeuvre pieces I'd inherited when Mother had passed away. Every item brought back memories of my youth, and especially of Isaac, and his sympathy card. I'd checked out the whereabouts of Isaac's business when I was investigating The Vine, and had also discovered where he lived, in a very upmarket district of Newcastle, just outside the city proper. My brother must have done very well indeed to be living out there among the wealthy industrialists, who made their fortunes out of the misery and grime of the city, but chose to live well out of it themselves. I thought that Isaac would be laughing at me, still living in a village pub, cooking meals for the gentry. The memories brought to mind the little lucky charm that old Kitty had given me on the day that I'd received my joinery papers from Mr Satterley, and I searched all the drawers in all of the pieces of furniture, finally finding it at the back of my own socks and undies drawer. I polished it up and fixed it onto my watch chain, thinking that maybe it would be a lucky omen for the move. The journey itself was a bit of a nightmare, using carts and the new-fangled petrol-driven lorries, which hissed and spouted steam, scaring all the local kids and dogs. Finally, however, after three or four days of upheaval, we took up residence in The Vine, all thoroughly exhausted!

A temporary landlord from the brewery was holding the fort, and he stayed for a fortnight after the move to show me the ropes. "They're a rough lot, Davy, but mostly decent folks; there's a few troublemakers, but you look as if you can handle a bit of rough stuff."

"No bother," I replied, and I told him about my time at the boys' home. "I think a few of the patrons have holidayed in there, so you'll be quite at home!" We had a pint and a laugh, and the fortnight passed slowly. I was impatient to take charge of the place myself. Grandma and Grandad did a fine job of sorting out the furniture and the living quarters, helped by Sally, who loved the idea of living in the big city. Arthur, of course, just got in everyone's way, and a local girl was hired to help. Her name was Ivy, one of a large family who lived nearby in the "Buildings," as the local tenements were called. She was a pleasant lass and Arthur liked her, which was a godsend, so I decided to ask if she would like a job as a barmaid in the evenings as well. She was delighted, saying that her mum needed all the money she could get, with so many kids to feed.

"Opening Night," as I called it on posters in the area, duly arrived, with myself in sole charge, and Ivy helping in the bar. I expected that a few of the patrons would try it on, to see what I was made of, and I wasn't disappointed! On opening the doors, there was a great influx of locals, eager to see what the new boy had to offer. Over the din made by the customers, I announced that the first pints were on me, and I was loudly applauded. A friendly atmosphere developed, and all was going well until a few of the young bloods tried a trick or two, as I knew they would. I quickly made it plain that I would take no nonsense, by unceremoniously throwing out the ringleader, and challenging the others to join in the fun! I got no takers, and was later well pleased with how the evening had passed. On counting the "take" from the till, I was delighted, telling Grandad that it would have taken a week or so to make that kind of money at the Red Lion, ham and egg teas included.

Things quickly settled down in The Vine, both landlord and customers well pleased with the way things were going. The only troubling aspect was the old folk. After the excitement of the move and getting the place organised, they couldn't settle, being afraid to go out for a walk, with all the traffic and "rough people," as they called them, as well as the constant noise, day and night. The smoky atmosphere caused by the factories and foundries soon began to affect Dad's emphysema, the old man coughing at times as though his lungs would burst. This, of course, worried Grandma to death, and I realised that they couldn't carry on like this for much longer. They'd never lived in any city before, even a clean one, and Newcastle was far from clean!

Help came from an unexpected source, a few months after we'd moved into The Vine. Aggie wrote to tell us that Fred had died suddenly of pneumonia. She'd thought it was just a bad cold, or flu, but it had turned nasty very suddenly, poor Fred hardly able to breathe, and the doctor came and said that he must go to hospital at once, but sadly it was too late for his life to be saved. The old folk and I went to the funeral in Manchester by train, with Charlie's family in Failsworth able to travel there by tram. The brewery sent in the same relief manager as before to hold the fort for a day or two, and so we stayed overnight at Aggie's, trying to comfort her. She was very distressed by the suddenness of her loss, and also by the fact that she would need to go back to teaching, in order to make ends meet. She didn't know anyone who could look after the youngsters, two of whom were still under school age. The bank would only pay her a small widow's pension, as Fred had not died in the line of duty, and she'd no idea how she would manage. I suddenly had a brainwave, and discussed it with Aggie once the old folk had gone to bed. She was delighted, and put my proposition to them the following morning. They could come and live with her, and look after the kids, so that she could go back to work, her teaching job providing enough to keep them all and pay the mortgage, which still had a long way to run. They gladly agreed, and remained in Manchester while I returned by train to Newcastle. I explained to Ivy that she would now have sole charge of the children, and would get a good pay rise accordingly, more than covering her lost bar work in the evenings. She was more than pleased, and I advertised at once for a barman to help me in the pub. The old couple settled down well at Aggie's, and Grandad's emphysema quickly abated, for even though Manchester was a city much bigger than Newcastle, the air was far cleaner, as Aggie's house was in a quiet, respectable suburb, with no mines or factories around to cause pollution. After a few months, however, Ivy announced that she was leaving, as she'd found a better job, cleaning and housekeeping for a wealthy old lady. I offered her a pay rise, but she admitted that it wasn't the money, but the children who had caused her to resign — they were too much for her, always quarrelling and fighting. I spoke to Sally, and of course she blamed Arthur, but

I knew that it was six of one and half a dozen of the other. At least the pub was doing good business, and Ron, the newly appointed barman, was a great asset. He knew all the locals, living nearby himself with his wife and kids, and took no snash from any of them, at the same time maintaining a cheery atmosphere, so the takings went up accordingly, and I was now making more money than I'd ever dreamt of. My new affluence gave me an idea, which I decided to try out on the children, or at least on Sally, who ruled the roost in that department. I asked her why she and Arthur were always quarrelling and fighting, and she informed me that it was because she was bored, and wanted to be with children her own age, not with a baby like Arthur. "What about your encyclopaedia, are you bored with that?" I asked, and she said no, but she had finished all the lessons and wanted to learn new things — could she have another tutor? The more I thought about this, the more I came to the same conclusion — the two children should go to school. They needed more fresh air and exercise, and couldn't get either at The Vine, where they couldn't play outdoors without supervision. I made enquiries and discovered that the Orme school was the top educational establishment in Newcastle. I promptly made an appointment to discuss matters with the headmaster, and was greatly impressed by the school building, but not by the headmaster, a stuck-up fool in my opinion, who clearly thought that a pub licensee and his kids would not fit in at his school. References would be required, and the children brought along for an interview. I contacted a few of my racing friends from Cranberry, who were happy to oblige with references, many of their children attending the Orme school as weekly boarders. I easily talked Sally into the idea of a "Posh School," where she would have lots of fun, with girls of her own age to play with. Arthur just said nothing, as usual, but I reckoned it was better if my son said nothing anyway — he only ever said the wrong thing if he bothered to speak at all.

The children were duly taken along for an interview, bathed and dressed in their best clothes. Sally immediately fell in love with the fine building, and chatted away happily, first with the headmaster, and then with the headmistress of the girls' department. I marvelled at her poise — it was almost as if she was interviewing them. Arthur, of course, never spoke, but Sally explained that he was very shy, and had told her that he really wanted to go to school and play with other boys. The references were handed over, and although the headmaster told me that I would hear in a week or two as to whether the children had been accepted or not, I was certain that they'd be offered a place, and bought chocolate and sweeties for the children as a reward for their good behaviour. I was not disappointed — two days later the acceptance forms arrived, and I heaved a huge sigh of relief. With the children sorted out in a way I was sure Emily would have approved of, I could concentrate on the pressing matters of running the pub, making money and returning to the sporting life that I had so enjoyed at Cranberry. I rubbed my wee pixie and thanked him again for bringing me luck. A school bus picked the children up each day outside the pub, and brought them back in the evening, to the cheers and jeers of the local kids, their ragged attire contrasting vividly to the plush uniforms of Sally and Arthur. I smiled to myself, thinking that the cost of those uniforms alone would have fed a local family for a couple of months, never mind the exorbitant fees. No matter, thanks to the generosity of the pub's clientele, I knew that I could afford it.

81

Despite flaunting my wealth, as one or two of my regulars muttered amongst themselves, I was a very popular landlord, for I could take a joke, pull a good pint, and have a laugh, my size and appearance ensuring that any would-be troublemakers would behave themselves or be banned.

The vast majority of the clientele were hard working, respectable people, who struggled to make an honest living; they didn't want a landlord who couldn't control the few wilder elements of their society. I soon made friends with most of my regulars, being especially drawn to a large family by the name of Bellingham — Ma and Pa and thirteen children- they drank like a shoal of fish, seemingly unaffected by the amount they consumed, and were always good for a laugh. Ronnie, my barman, knew them well, and said that they were very kind, hospitable people, telling me that a year or so earlier, they had legally adopted a local girl, who had been left an orphan by the sudden death of her parents, and who would otherwise have been sent to an orphanage. Ma Bellingham had laughed about it, saying that you don't notice one more when you've already got twelve of the little blighters! Everything in my garden was rosy, except for one thing — I began to feel the need for female companionship again! There was a good selection of attractive young women frequenting The Vine, and quite a few of them gave me the glad eye, but remembering Beattie, I thought I'd be better off choosing an older woman — after all, I was fast approaching middle age myself, God forbid! My eye began to rest on one of the Bellingham girls, Gertrude by name. I thought that she was in her late twenties or early thirties, on viewing her when she came into the pub with other members of her family. She behaved in a very ladylike fashion, never having too much to drink. I enquired of some of the regulars as to whether she was married, but they all said no, she was a bit of an odd one, why didn't I ask Ronnie, who knew her better than they did. Ron smiled when I approached him on the matter, saying he'd wondered if the boss was interested, as he'd noticed the glances I gave her when I thought no one was looking. She'd never married, but had a "good job", as Ron put it, being private secretary to a businessman twice her age in Newcastle. On enquiring how old she was, I was surprised to learn that she was in her late thirties, the eldest of the Bellingham girls. I was quite relieved on discovering that she had a male friend, as I was beginning to wonder if she preferred female companions.

"God no," Ron laughed, "She's had a few blokes in her time, but doesn't want to settle down, according to her brothers. She likes to enjoy herself, without the responsibilities of kids, cooking and housework — can't say I blame her!" I decided that I'd like to get to know her better, as she sounded just right for me — companionship without commitments!

The next time she came into the pub, I made a point of speaking to her, very low key, just friendly conversation. A week later, she came in again, and I noticed that she'd had her hair done, and had made herself up carefully. I chuckled to myself — I was on the right track, at last! She came in yet again the following week, and I got into conversation with her, this time asking what her preferences were amongst Newcastle's finest hotels. She seemed well acquainted with them all, and said she liked nothing better than a good meal in pleasant surroundings. I asked if she would be kind enough to accompany me for a meal at the hotel of her choice, and she replied that she'd be happy to, but would need plenty of notice, as she had other commitments, as she put it! We duly "stepped out" the following week, and I happily left the pub in Ron's capable hands. The evening was a great success, and we enjoyed smoked salmon as a starter, followed by fillet of beef, and tried a couple of bottles, one red, one white, of a very fine wine, recommended by the waiter. I boggled when I got the bill, thinking that I should have gone into upmarket hotel keeping instead of the pub trade, selling beer and pies! Gertrude had clearly taken pains with her appearance, as I had myself, in my best suit with my father's gold watch adorning my waistcoat. We had been picked up at The Vine, and later returned there, by one of the new-fangled taxi cabs, and then I walked her home to the Bellinghams. We kissed goodnight in the doorway, and I suggested that we must repeat our enjoyable night out. I walked back to the pub with a spring in my step, and winked at Ron, who was still clearing up after the crowd had left. "Good night, boss," he called, and he wasn't just being polite!

Chapter 8
Worrying News

I booked a meal for us in another of the fine hotels in the city, but had to call it off when I received a worrying letter from Annie Cooke, Charlie's wife. She said that she hated asking me for a favour, but she was desperate; Charlie's pay had gone rapidly downhill, as the seam they were working was running out. Much worse, however, was the fact that they no longer had poor Gertie's wage from the weaving shed, as she'd been injured in an accident, and had needed to have her arm amputated! I felt sick, and was furious with myself for not keeping in regular touch with my best friend! I asked one of the Bellinghams to let Gertrude know that something important had come up, and that I couldn't keep our date, but would contact her when I got back. I got Sally and Arthur to promise to behave, and get themselves ready for school every morning, and asked Ron to see that they got something to eat each evening. "Are you all right to hold the fort, Ron," I asked, "or should I try to get the relief guy in for a day or two?"

"No way, boss — I'll manage fine, and I can always get one of the Bellingham lassies to lend a hand in the evening, if we're mad busy. You go see what's up at your friend's place, and we'll be fine!" I left early next morning, worried to death, but praying that there was something I could do. I took a big pile of notes out of the safe and decided that I'd get Charlie to accept the cash, even if I had to stick it down his throat!

I reached Failsworth by train and taxi before Charlie got home from the pit, thank God! I took Annie into my arms and told her how sorry I was for not having written more often. Through her tears of surprise at seeing me so soon after her letter, and telling me that she should never have written it, and that Charlie would be so angry when he found out what she'd done, I managed to tell her that I had brought a wad of cash with me, and she must always tell me if she ever needed more. I was just pressing it into her protesting hands when Charlie arrived, and with far from a friendly greeting, looked at me like thunder, asking what the hell was going on? "Before you get on your high horse, Charlie Cooke, let me give you a word of advice — you say one wrong word to Annie about the cash I've brought, and I'll deck you, pal or no pal. She had the good sense to let me know about Gertie's so-called accident, asking if I could help, and I'm helping the only way I know how! I blame myself for losing touch for a while, so busy with settling into The Vine, but I also blame you for not keeping in touch with me. What's your excuse?" He sat down with his head in his hands, and Annie said that she'd make a cup of tea and headed into the kitchen. "Tell me about what happened to cause Gertie's so-called accident," I insisted, "and what are you doing about it? Have you taken advice from her union? I assume she belonged to one?"

"Her so-called union is useless, Davy. They took it up with the weaving firm, but were told that it was her fault, carelessness! A piece of wood on the loom flew off, hitting her arm — how could that have been her fault?"

"What do her workmates say?" I demanded. "They saw what happened, didn't they?"

"Oh aye, but they wouldn't say owt — they're all scared for their jobs!"

"Are you just going to take this lying down, Charlie? That's not like you pal, I must say. Poor Gertie will be lucky to ever work again, with only one arm, her right arm, so Annie was telling me, and what about marriage prospects? Her whole life could be ruined, lad!"

"I know, so you needn't rub it in. I've been in touch with my union, the mineworkers, and they're looking into it. A bloke came round last week, and I think that he was one of us, although he was supposed to be from the government. He took statements from her pals who'd seen what happened, and they say that they told him that the place was a death trap, because he'd assured them that there would be no reprisals. "The government are collecting information," he said, "about accidents to minors in the workplace, and I've informed the bosses here that I will be reporting this incident to the proper authorities!"

"Well, thank God for that!" I sank back in my chair. "I'm sorry I flew off the handle a bit, Charlie. I should have known you wouldn't let it rest. Now, let's have that cup of tea, and we can talk about happier things, and then perhaps I can meet the family — where is Gertie, by the way?"

"Up in her bedroom. She doesn't come out of it much, she's so conscious of her injury, poor lass!" He then put his head in his hands, and I could tell that he was crying like a baby. I stayed the night, sleeping on the sofa, and went home the next day a sadder and wiser man. Not every problem could be solved by money, and poor Charlie was heartbroken for his lovely girl.

When I got home, Ronnie welcomed me, hoping that all

was well. I said that we'd have to wait and see, but at least things were moving in the right direction. I didn't go into details with him, or the kids, but when I next met Gertrude over dinner, I told her the whole sorry story. She said it was a terrible thing to happen to a young girl, but life was full of tragedies, and sometimes we just had to take what was thrown at us. I'd expected a rather more sympathetic response to my niece's plight, but told myself that the Bellinghams had probably suffered many setbacks in their large family, and had perhaps become stoical about such things.

Chapter 9
Wartime

We continued going out for dinner, and Gertrude was always a very pleasant companion, but she soon made it clear that she was not the marrying kind. She enjoyed her life and her independence, and had no desire for children of her own; after all, look at her poor mother, worn out by a baby every year! Our dinners in fine hotels were soon followed by overnight stays in those same establishments, but I had to promise to take all necessary precautions. Her indifference only made me keener, so I plied her with supplications and nice, but not ostentatious items of jewellery. One evening, snuggling up in the fine bedroom of the hotel where we had earlier dined well, and perhaps partaken of a little too much of the fine wine, Gertrude finally succumbed to my frequent pleas of undying love, and said that she would marry me, but on one condition — she would not supply me with another child. I laughed and assured her that she need not worry. As I said, I had two already, so why would I want more?

The year was 1914, and war was looming, with nations throwing threats about like tennis balls. Charlie, of course, got deferment from military service as a miner, and his son, young Charlie, now a trainee at the pit, could probably have qualified for deferment, but actually wanted to join up, "to see the world," as he put it, much to his father's annoyance. I also got deferment, as I was the father of two motherless children, and Gertrude laughingly pointed out that it was a good job that she'd refused my many proposals, for if we'd married sooner, I would have been called up! Tommy the horse was not so lucky, however, for despite his great age, he was requisitioned and led away to sail for France. He'd never been happy in Newcastle, as he was afraid of motorised vehicles, with their klaxons and fumes, and I hoped that he would pass away peacefully before he got to a war zone. Early in 1915, our engagement was announced in The Vine, to the joyous cheers of the clientele. Most of them had obtained deferment, as they worked in factories or foundries, which had been requisitioned by the government to make arms for the soldiers fighting in Europe. The war was dragging on, with the army getting bogged down in France. It was turning out to be a disaster, and not the brief skirmish that everybody had thought it would be. A small wedding was planned for the following month, as we thought such an occasion would buck everyone up, and it certainly did, the locals all of the opinion that a happy event would occur a few months later. Gertrude and I were equally amused, knowing that no such event would occur, and that the regulars would be disappointed, as no christening celebrations would follow. Sally and Arthur were told that they would soon have a new mother, but they received the news with complete indifference. They didn't know Gertrude, and were completely taken up with the activities at their school. In any case, their sad experience with Emily had done nothing to make them want to repeat it; not even the promise of new wedding clothes interested them. I sensed that Gertrude felt the same about my children as they did about her. Ah well, an amicable indifference was better than outright hostility, I reckoned. The wedding duly took place, the children behaving admirably, and being rewarded with bags of "goodies", which they took up to their room at the first opportunity. The reception was held in the pub, all the regulars being invited, together with several members of the gentry, along with their wives. A great deal of liquor was consumed, a good time had by all, and Gertrude and I consummated our marriage with a frolicsome wedding night, which unfortunately resulted in Gertrude becoming pregnant! She was very unhappy about this, surprising me with her "over reaction," as I saw it. Very well, I'd known that she didn't want a child, but surely it wasn't that important? She wouldn't have to look after it, if she didn't want to. We would hire a nursemaid or nanny for the baby, and it would be bottle fed, if that was what Gertrude preferred. I tried to jolly her along, but sadly to no avail. She found fault with everything, blaming me and the whole world for her condition. She demanded that several of her family be banned from the pub, for no good reason, and took particular exception to Arthur, now a schoolboy of ten years old. She accused him of pinching her cigarettes, but he denied it vigorously. She said he'd be selling them at his posh school, and when I asked, "Why would he, as he gets plenty of pocket money?" she replied, "That is what's wrong with the children — they are grossly over-indulged!" Sally was upsetting her applecart as well, demanding that she be allowed to apply for university, as some of her friends were doing. Gertrude said that the fees for university were preposterous, a ridiculous waste of money, what with the tuition fees and the cost of boarding away from home. "She only wants to get away from here, so she can chase some rich lad she's set her cap at, David; she's lad mad, so my friends tell me!"

"There're not many rich lads round here, love," I laughed, trying to ease the tension, but she replied that the lad in question didn't live in Newcastle. "He only visits occasionally, as his family owns the Blue Buildings, and live in Norfolk, wherever that is!" She became more and more depressed as her pregnancy wore on, and even her family became tired of her "nonsense," as they called it. I began to worry that history was repeating itself, and sure enough, a few months later, she passed away, whilst giving birth to a baby girl, who also sadly died two days later, both being buried together. I was devastated for a second time, and vowed never to marry again. I had to organise another funeral, a small affair this time, due to wartime restrictions, and the relatives could not come, as the trains were commandeered by the Army to transport soldiers. Young Charlie had got his wish for excitement, and had left for France with the Failsworth Lads Brigade, which upset Charlie senior, but at least there was better news regarding Gertie. It seemed that the bloke Charlie thought had come from the miners' union had actually been from the government, who had set up an investigation into employment accidents, specifically among the under sixteens. The miners' union had simply given the information to the Textile Workers Association, who had then acted upon it, and Gertie was to receive a lump sum, and a pension. "God knows when," Charlie said, "but at least there's something in the pipeline, if this bloody war doesn't knock it on the head!" I frequently offered to send more money to Annie, but she always refused, saying that Charlie was making more money again at the pit, as new seams had been opened, coal being badly needed for the war effort.

I felt that my spirits were getting lower and lower, and

knew that I'd have to buck myself up. I was certainly never going to look for another woman again, and so decided to turn my attention to other "pleasurable" activities; I started to drink heavily, trying to drown my sorrows, and spent less and less time working at the pub. I was more often to be seen at the local "shoots" and racecourses, betting heavily with my posh friends, and usually losing heavily to boot. Ronnie managed the pub very efficiently, and if he took a few bob out of the till at closing time, he'd earned it, in my opinion. He suggested to me that he needed a responsible barmaid to help him out on my frequent absences, and knew just the girl, Edith, the Bellinghams' youngest daughter. I told him immediately to put her on the payroll, and all went well. She was pretty and efficient, and I no longer felt guilty about my shooting trips and race days. I went AWOL from The Vine even more often to shooting parties, and to the races, where I gambled heavily, constantly trying to recoup my previous losses. I finally realised that something had to change; I couldn't carry on in this manner, but I also couldn't give up my new lifestyle. One day, when I was at the races, an idea struck me. The only betting at the time was through the Tote at the courses themselves, and if ordinary folk wanted a bet, they had to get a "posh nob" to put it on for them. I decided to test the water, and let it be known at The Vine, that I would place customers' bets, if they so wished, at the Tote, and collect their winnings for them. They could check the results in the papers the next day, so there was no possibility of them being cheated. The idea went down very well with the clientele, and soon I was collecting large amounts of money to put on horses at big race meetings. I placed the bets, collected the winnings, and took the money back to the pub to pay out to the happy punters, who then proceeded to drink away their good fortune, the winnings going into the Vine's tills. Everybody was happy, except when their horses lost, but of course no one could blame the landlord for that!

The new income gave me a real boost; I began to feel myself again, and indeed my only real concern was Sally, now a pretty young girl, who dressed and acted more like a twenty-year-old. She had always been the apple of my eye, and often skipped school to accompany me to race meetings, drawing admiring glances from the younger male racegoers, much to my amusement. She paid no attention to these young blades, however, and I was sure that she had no interest in laddies yet, which was as it should be, as she was still only fifteen. She had changed her mind about going to university, even though I had been coming round to the idea, and left school against my wishes, getting a job at Boots the Chemists, where she could train to become a pharmacist. I couldn't understand her changing her mind so radically, or her frequent mood swings, one minute full of the joys, the next down in the dumps. Friends told me that this was normal with her age group, so I didn't worry unduly. I didn't know, however, that my darling daughter had fallen for a cousin of her best friend from school, Millie Wardle. Randles Wardle was his somewhat unusual name, and I soon discovered, whilst reading her diary one day while she was out at work, that Sally was totally obsessed with this young man. I realised then that Gertrude's story was nearer the truth than I had imagined. I made enquiries among my racing friends, and discovered that the aforementioned Wardles came to Newcastle periodically, to check on how the family businesses were doing. They owned the Blue Buildings, amongst other properties, and were "very well-to-do," according to the Bellinghams, who lived there, but they were also "decent landlords, who didn't put the rent up every other day!" They seemed to know what Sally was up to, but didn't tell me about the local gossip, regarding her antics. I decided to broach the subject one evening when she was home, and not working on her studies for her pharmacy course. I had hoped for some reassurances but was left disappointed. Sally informed me that she was in love with Randles, and would marry him or die trying. I told her not to be ridiculous, as Randles came from a very wealthy family, and was much older than her anyway! I had discovered that the lad was a pilot in the newly formed air force, and laughed, saying that there would be a long queue of silly young women like herself, all vying for his attentions — she didn't stand a chance! The crunch came when Sally didn't come home for three nights, and I became concerned. I knew that she often stayed over at her friend Millie's, but never for as long as this, so I contacted Millie, who told me that Sally had run away to Norfolk to meet Randles, without telling me or even leaving me a note. I was furious, and set off at once to find her, and bring her back home, obtaining the young man's address from a reluctant Millie. I returned a couple of days later with an unrepentant Sally, and informed her that I had brought her home for her own safety and reputation, but would never do so again. If she ever ran away in future, I would leave her to her fate. She duly absconded a few weeks later, and I made no attempt to retrieve her. She returned home from time to time, usually when she had run short of money. She got a job at the Boots headquarters in Kettering, and was never pregnant, thank God! I always expected that this would be the outcome. She had known Gertrude, of course, but hadn't liked her at all, expressing no sympathy when she died, merely telling me that I should have looked before I leapt, which I thought was rich coming from her! She met Edith, but the pair didn't get along, as Sally thought that I had replaced Gertrude with this young girl, a ridiculous thing to do for a man of my age! She finally left the family in 1919, going abroad to continue her pursuit of Randles, who was now in the newly formed RAF, occasionally sending a postcard from exotic places. Despite everything, I still adored her, forever the apple of my eye, and I wouldn't hear a word against her.

On the brighter side, things had radically improved for the Cooke household in Failsworth. The family had finally received compensation for Gertie's injury, and had used the money to buy two houses at one end of their row. These houses were larger than the mid-terrace house that they'd lived in before, so they converted the end one into a corner shop for Gertie, and all lived above that, with the other house being rented out, to pay for a mortgage on it. I had asked a lawyer friend for advice on this procedure, and guided Charlie through the process. Gertie loved serving in the shop, and gradually returned to being the confident young woman she had been before her injury. Things had not gone so well for Charlie junior, however, who had returned home a broken young man, suffering terrible nightmares. He was also unable to hold down a job of any kind, completely devastated by the horrors he had witnessed during his time as a soldier.

Helping the Cooke family get through their time of trouble enabled me to regain some of my good spirits, and I returned to being the jovial landlord that I had been before Gertrude's untimely death. My clientele were delighted, and things at The Vine returned to normal, jolly and welcoming once again. A few of the girls who drank in the Vine began to flirt with me, and I enjoyed their attentions, but had no wish to get involved again. Marriage and David Brindley did not get along together, I had decided, and I stuck to my resolution — no more women in my life! I tried to get to know my son, Arthur, no longer a funny little boy, but he had other ideas. He was still officially a pupil at Orme Boys' School, but I had discovered that he seldom attended that expensive establishment, preferring to spend his time playing snooker in a local club. Several of the clientele also played there, and told me that my boy had a natural talent, but I took no notice, thinking that they were just saying that to get into my good books. I pointed out to Arthur that he was just wasting the opportunities that his expensive education had given him, but he just laughed and said, "Oh, you mean like Sally!" I was tempted to give him a clout, but realised that this would do more harm than good, so I contented myself by saying that it was up to him what he did with his life, and he could leave school at the end of this term, if that was what he wanted. "I am not going to continue paying the fees, if you can't even be bothered to attend!" Arthur just laughed and said, "Thanks, Dad, now I'll have more time to practise! Could you buy me a decent cue with the money you'll save?"

"Buy your own bloody cue, lad, with all the money you're winning," I said, walking away before I said something I'd regret. It infuriated me that my children, both of them, were happy to throw away the opportunities that I had given them, and wondered then what Emily would have said about my parenting skills. I'd given them both money, and in Sally's case, love as well, and look where it had got me; they both despised me, and I knew very well what Emily would have

97

said — You gave them money, David, but you didn't give them your time or attention. You were always too busy working or enjoying yourself. You spoilt Sally with overindulgence, and you neglected Arthur, making him feel that you didn't care what he did — let them both go their own ways now, don't interfere with their hopes and plans, it's too late. Just try to help them if they'll let you, and remember, they are both our children, and I trust that now you'll do better, love!

I consulted one of my snooker-playing friends a few days later, and bought the cue that he recommended, leaving it in Arthur's bedroom without a word. The next morning, Arthur came down for breakfast, a rare event in itself, and said, "Thanks Dad, the cue's a beauty!" He actually smiled at me, and in him I could see Emily smiling too. I'd never noticed before how much Arthur resembled his mother! The snooker players among the clientele told me that Arthur's playing had gone from strength to strength with the new cue, and there was a rumour that Joe Davis, a young professional player, had been booked to come and give an exhibition at the club. Word was going round that if he did come, Arthur would be chosen to play him. "We'll keep you up to speed, Davy. You should come and watch your lad, though, you'd be proud as punch!" I smiled, but said that I'd enough to do at the pub, keeping everyone in order. I secretly didn't want to encourage my son too much, as I still hoped that Arthur would find a profession he fancied.

Ron and young Edith Bellingham were a great team behind the bar, and I found myself watching Edith more and more — at first, because I constantly compared her to Sally, as she was only a couple of years older than my daughter. She worked like a Trojan with Ronnie, and yet always seemed to have time for a laugh and a joke with the customers, many of whom, of course, belonged to her own family. She was delighted on paydays when she checked her earnings — you'd have thought that I'd given her the Crown Jewels, yet Sally would have considered the amount trifling, barely enough to buy her a good lipstick, and would certainly not have said thank you to me. I slowly began to make much of "young Edith," as she was called by the customers, noticing that several of the young blades obviously fancied her, but had got no joy in that department. I occasionally bought her little presents of make up or paste jewellery, that she could wear in the pub, and as I paid her more attention, I noticed that she only appeared to have two dresses to wear at work. "One on my back and one in the washtub," she laughed when I mentioned it. The following payday, she gasped when she saw how much she had earned, and told me that there must have been a mistake. I smiled, telling her to buy herself a new frock or two to wear at work. "Maybe one of the lads will propose, and we'll have a wedding in no time!" She laughed, and went over to show her mother how much she'd earned, and they had a good giggle together. I wished that I could have heard what they were laughing about, but I was called over by a few of the punters, who wanted to place their bets for the races the following day. When I got back with the winnings, my pockets full of money for the delighted clientele, I saw that Edith was wearing a pretty new dress, and her mother gave me a knowing wink as I passed her. A good time was had by all, and when the last of the happy punters were leaving, I told Edith that she looked tired, after all the running about she'd been doing, carrying trays of drinks, and she could stay over if she liked. She agreed, saying that her feet were killing her, and that was that! I was pretty sloshed myself, and later that night, much to both of our amazements, I asked her to marry me. To my delight, she accepted immediately, laughing and saying that she had thought I'd never ask. We married two months later, with Arthur as best man. Edith and Arthur got on really well, so different from Arthur and Gertrude, and I felt happier than I had in a long time. My troubles were over, and I could settle down for a comfortable middle age.

Chapter 10
Disaster

At first, all the omens pointed to a bright future for myself and my new bride — our reception in The Vine was a happy affair, just the pub crowd invited, and Arthur proposed the toast to the happy couple. He was now a happy lad himself, for Joe Davis had indeed given an exhibition at the snooker club, and Arthur had been chosen to play him, as expected. He narrowly beat Joe, again as expected, for Arthur had told me that the visitor always lets his opponent win on these occasions. I hadn't gone along, pleading pressure of work, and Arthur told me that he was actually thankful for that. My presence would have made him nervous, and he'd probably have lost, despite Joe's best efforts to let him win. I knew different, however, as some of my racing cronies had been present, meeting the visitor later in his hotel at a small reception held for him. Joe had told them that Arthur was the best player he'd ever come across — the lad could have beaten him for real on two separate occasions during the game, if he'd had a little more experience. I felt very proud of my son, but couldn't bring myself to tell him, still feeling that my boy should be aiming for something more respectable than becoming world snooker champion!

During the summer, The Vine had two unannounced visits from the brewery representatives. I didn't know these gentlemen, but made sure that they were well entertained, and handed over the books as requested. I told them that I would have preferred some notice of the visit, as was normal, but if they didn't mind my scrawl and crossings out, that was all right by me! I asked after the usual bloke, but was told that he had been ill, and had retired prematurely. I wondered about this, as the guy had been in fine fettle on his last visit, only a few months earlier. Ron was also concerned by these visits, and the thought crossed my mind that maybe he too had been skimming the cream off the top a little bit more than usual.

When the men left, taking copies of "relevant passages," as they called them, I took a closer look at the figures, and was alarmed to find that they were much worse than I had feared. I knew that there was a shortfall, there had been for a couple of years, but I'd always been able to "massage" the books in readiness for inspection. I told myself not to panic, and tried to behave as normal with Ron, but I watched him closely, and checked everything thoroughly from week to week. I was dismayed to find that my trusted barman had been on the take for almost as long as he'd been employed at the pub. I called him into the parlour one day in July, when Edith was out with her girlfriends, and confronted him with the figures. "Things don't add up, Ron," I said quietly. "What's been going on, lad?" At first, Ron denied any wrongdoing, but when he saw that I knew exactly what he'd been up to, he tried to bluff his way out. "I've done no more than you," he blustered, "and if we don't stick together, I can prove that you've been at it as well!" At this point, I laid my cards on the table. I pointed out that I was well in with the police, making regular generous contributions to their benevolent fund, so it would be easy for me to blame him for all of the shortfall. Being a well-respected man and landlord, who hobnobbed with the Gentry, I knew that they too would vouch for my honesty and upright character. Having made a few discreet enquiries, I had discovered that Ron had a less than perfect reputation, having done time for burglary in his younger days. The poor man tried to threaten me for a little while longer, but then gave up and begged me not to prosecute — he had a family to support, and they would be in the poor house if he was imprisoned. I genuinely liked the fellow, and knew that we were equally to blame, so I told him to get out and never come back. "Just tell everybody that we've had a blazing row, Ron, and that you've handed in your notice." He departed, thanking me for my understanding, and also for the wad of notes that I had ready for him in an envelope. That solved the immediate problem, but I knew that I would have to come up with a great deal of money, in double quick time. To add to my woes, Tojo, my faithful hound, came home the next day, dragging his hind legs behind him, whimpering piteously. I took him to the farrier's, who said that there was nothing to be done, other than put the poor animal out of his misery. I immediately suspected Ron of taking his revenge, but on asking around, I discovered that Ron and his family had left the district on the same evening that he'd "given his notice." They owed a good deal of rent, and had done a moonlight flit. I never got to the bottom of Tojo's injuries, and Edith said a prayer for the faithful dog's soul, lighting a candle and putting it in the pub's window. I had to smile at her kindness and childlike innocence — I knew that I was a lucky man to have won her hand. I continued my playboy lifestyle, however, even making enquiries into finding a young gun dog to replace Tojo. I reckoned that any change in my ways would arouse suspicion in the minds of the bank's investigators, and my clientele at The Vine. I confided in no one, not even Edith or Arthur, and placed bets on "certs" that only occasionally lived up to their reputations, knowing that the axe could fall at any moment if I didn't get a big winner soon! Arthur, the budding snooker champion, now seventeen, had heard rumours of my impending downfall, but of course he'd heard such rumours before, and they had always come to nothing. He told me later that it amused him, in a funny kind of way, for he felt I'd never bothered about him or his hopes for the future, so why should he care what happened to me? On the other hand, he knew he wasn't making enough money in the snooker halls yet to support himself. He needed to get out of small-time Newcastle and strut his stuff in the big cities, such as Manchester, Birmingham or Liverpool, for starters. He also cared about what would happen to Edith if I were declared bankrupt, possibly even going to prison for theft. All the locals, with the exception of her family, said that she'd only married me for my money, and although that was possibly true, he really liked her. She was not his type, but kind and good fun, so different from her nowty big sister.

The crunch came sooner than any of us had expected. Arthur could see that I'd come up with one of my schemes, as I'd regained my jaunty demeanour, whistling away as I cleared up when the last of the clientele had left. The talk in the pubs and snooker halls was that I had sorted out my problems by getting rid of that rogue, Ron, who they all knew had been robbing me blind. I'd never kept my finger on the pulse, they all reckoned, but I'd obviously sorted everything out, and things were now back to normal. I was off to the races regularly again, leaving Edith to cope, with one of her many brothers lending a hand; or failing that, she occasionally roped in Arthur himself, who enjoyed the banter and basked in the new-found esteem of the locals, since his "victory" over Joe Davis. "Imagine that," they laughed, "The soon to be Champion snooker player who serves in our pub!" I continued to place the bets for the clientele as usual, and even appeared to be on a winning streak at the racecourses, regularly bringing home winners for the punters. Everything in the garden was rosy again, or that's how it seemed!

The axe fell with the Cesarewitch at Newmarket in October 1922. Arthur didn't know what I was up to, but realised that it must be something big. The guys from the brewery had been round again, but I appeared to have bluffed my way through this latest investigation, blaming Ron for everything, saying that he'd disappeared, taking his family and the brewery's profits with him. Everything was friendly enough when the men left, and I was pleased with my performance. I'd also had the "insider" tip-off to end all tip-offs — straight from the horse's mouth, so to speak. Arthur later learned that the horse hadn't told me anything, but some of my wealthy pals had. A racehorse, with the curious name of Tishy, had come in last in the race the previous year, but the feeling amongst the upper-crust punters was that the horse had been nobbled. She was owned by the Rothschild family, and had a brilliant pedigree, coming from a long line of winners, but must have been 'got at' before the race. Coming in last meant that the odds of her winning the race this year were very high, so the payoff would be great if she pulled it off, which she would, as she'd be guarded like royalty prior to the big race. I told no one of my plan, and encouraged the clientele to bet on the sure-fire favourite, Light Dragoon, telling them I was doing the same, even though the odds were very short.

The pub was packed with expectant punters when I returned home, and I paid out their winnings, calling for a free drink all round to celebrate the win. After a couple of these, everyone was very merry, and the party went on until long after closing time, until I managed to usher the well-oiled clientele out. When they had all left, singing and shouting happily, I locked up, and suggested to Edith and Arthur that the three of us should have a night cap and a chat. Edith poured the drinks, happy as a cat lapping cream, and Arthur, seizing his chance, suggested that his father might give him a share of the loot, so that he could go to Manchester to try his luck on the snooker circuit there. Edith shouted her approval from the bar. "Let's just enjoy our drink first, before we get carried away," I replied, and Arthur must have heard the warning bells ring. "Something up, Dad?" he enquired, and I laughed, rather too loudly. "You could say so, son! Here goes — I didn't bet on the favourite, but put my money on Tishy, who did her usual and came in last! Never trust a horse that crosses its legs! All of our money is up the spout! My bloody insiders got it wrong again, so let's enjoy this drink, as it may be our last for a very long time!" Nobody spoke, as Arthur tried to take in what my words meant, Edith grasping it before him, and bursting into tears. "What the hell are we going to do, Davy?"

"It's all right, love, I've got a plan," I said, stroking her hair in an attempt to comfort her. She only wailed all the louder, until I reached the end of my tether, shouting, "For God's sake, Edith, shut up and listen!"

"This had better be good," Arthur said. We were to wait for an hour or so, switching off all the lights, to make it look as though we'd gone to bed. Then, in the small hours, we would leave the pub with what we stood up in, the only luggage being some jewellery inherited from my mother, good stuff that we'd be able to sell for a considerable sum of money. We would walk to the main station, and catch the first train to Manchester. From there we would go to Aunt Aggie's and stay with her until the heat had died down. She had a big house, and we'd given her plenty of good times in Cranberry. "She doesn't know me," wailed Edith, but I calmed her down, saying, "You're my wife, love, and she'll be delighted to meet you!"

We left the Vine at two thirty a.m. and trudged through the quiet streets in silence, unnoticed except by a few curious cats, arriving at the station at three forty a.m. I kept checking the time, which irritated Arthur, as it told him how worried I was. The first Manchester train wasn't due to leave until six thirty a.m., so we huddled in the waiting room, praying that no one would come in and recognise us. Edith fell asleep, and that gave Arthur the chance to ask me what I thought the Bellinghams would do, if they caught up with us. "Why nowt, lad, they'll soon simmer down!"

"Then why are we running away?" He didn't understand, until I spelt it out. "We're running away so that I don't get arrested, when the brewery checks the books again. There's an enormous hole in the takings, and they'll get the police involved. I'll be arrested and charged with defrauding them, found guilty and imprisoned. Does that answer your question, son?"

"Does Edith realise all that, Dad?"

"Of course not, she believed me when I told her that Ron had been pilfering, which of course he had, but nothing like as much as I had. I paid him to disappear and carry the can, but now everything's gone from bad to worse. Why do you think

I didn't let you bring your cue? That would have been a dead giveaway, big chap and young couple, the lad carrying a snooker cue! But don't worry, son, it'll all blow over; there's been worse disasters at sea!" We didn't speak again until the train pulled in, waking Edith up with its huffing and puffing. A few other passengers boarded, thankfully no one we knew, and we feigned sleep all the way to our destination at Manchester Central. I took charge, saying "so far, so good. Now all we have to do is get ourselves to Aggie's house. I've been there before, but I took a taxi from here, as I was bringing Grandma and Grandad Cooke to stay." I led them to the information desk, where we were informed by the clerk that we should catch the number 27 bus, which left from just outside the station in about twenty or so minutes. So it was, that on the day the Cesarewitch results appeared in the papers, and all hell broke loose outside The Vine, as the pub remained closed, Edith, Arthur and I were safely ensconced in Aunt Aggie's kitchen, drinking tea and some of Grandma's hot soup. Our troubles were behind us, or so we thought.

When Aggie arrived home from her teaching job, she was amazed to find us installed in her parlour, chatting to Grandma and Grandad Cooke. A few minutes later, her three children arrived home as well, all together, and bringing a couple of friends from university home with them. The children were all now students, studying English, Law and Mathematics respectively, and were quickly shooed upstairs by Aggie. The parlour was much smaller than I had remembered, and we could all barely fit into it. The house itself appeared to have shrunk, but of course, the young people were now much bigger than when I'd seen them last. Once they had gone, I explained to Aggie that, due to a misunderstanding, my wife Edith, whom I introduced briefly, Arthur and myself had found it necessary to leave Newcastle in a bit of a hurry, and wondered if we could stay with the family for a week or two, until the problem could be sorted out. Aggie didn't know where to look, and I saw that she was terribly embarrassed, so I decided to make it as easy as possible for her. "I can see that you're a bit tight for space, Aggie, now that the kids have grown up. I wouldn't have recognised them if I'd met them on the street. Arthur's the same, as you can see, but whereas your children are studying hard to provide for their future, he's wasting his time trying to become world snooker champion, and Sally's run off chasing some rich lad, instead of improving her qualifications in chemistry, as I would have wished. Such is life, is it not? I can well see that you haven't room for three more folk here, but can I ask you to put us up for one night? We didn't get much sleep on the train, and would be glad to rest up here, and then we'll go to your Charlie's place; I believe that he has two houses now!"

"Yes, he does," Aggie replied, looking mightily relieved at my suggestion. "I can give you some blankets and you can rest in here, the three of you, on the sofa and in the armchairs. We've only got three bedrooms, and two of them are on the small side, and me and the kids need them all, what with me having marking to do, and the kids their studying and essays and such like. Will that be all right?"

"Of course." I smiled. "But what about Grandma and Grandad, where will they sleep?"

"Oh, they have a 'put you up' in the kitchen. I make it up for them every night."

"I quite see your difficulty," I said, "how about if I give you a couple of quid to get something for us all for dinner, and perhaps a couple of bottles of beer, and then we can have a merry evening, before we all settle down to sleep?"

"That would be lovely, David!" Aggie smiled weakly, and I saw that she was probably struggling to make ends meet, what with her mortgage and six mouths to feed. I decided to speak to Charlie about it tomorrow, when the three of us got to Failsworth. Arthur and Aggie's boy were dispatched to get a few beers and pies for tea, and a pleasant evening was passed, but I felt that everything was far from rosy in this "posh" house, that didn't much resemble a home.

We travelled to Failsworth the following morning, still half asleep, and wondered what our welcome would be like at Charlie and Annie's — we needn't have worried! A delighted Annie welcomed us in with hugs and kisses all round. She said that Charlie would have a great laugh when he got home from the pit, and fed us with the tasty remains of the previous night's stew, running through to help Gertie in the shop when it got busy. Bessie arrived home first, also elated to see the unexpected visitors, and then Charlie, black as the hobs of Hell! He couldn't believe his eyes on seeing me, and rushed in to shake my hand. Annie just managed to stop him giving me a bear hug, and ordered him into the backyard. "No bath by the fire tonight, Charlie Cooke, not with visitors present!" I protested on my friend's behalf, but to no avail, and Charlie scrubbed himself down outside in the tin tub. While this was going on, I sent Arthur out to the nearby pub, Charlie's local, to get some beers and a bottle of whisky. "Where's the money come from?" Arthur enquired. "The till at The Vine, where do you think? The locals all blew their winnings, thank God! How did you imagine I paid for the railway tickets?" Annie produced a large meat and potato pie, the same as the one she brought to the Red Lion in Cranberry, and we all ate our fill, especially enjoying the rhubarb and custard to follow. "Our Annie's a magician, Davy, she can always rustle up summat out of nowt!" Charlie smiled fondly at his wife, and for the first time in my life, I envied my friend; few possessions, no prospects, no money, but happiness aplenty, and a happiness that had lasted for many years. Arthur was more interested in his cousins, now two very pretty young ladies. He had sympathy for Gertie, having only one arm, although she didn't seem bothered or embarrassed by that fact, but it was her sister Bessie who stood out especially, with her flaming red hair. I could see that my son was smitten!

Next day, I walked to the Failsworth railway station. It was on the main line from Leeds to Manchester and had a regular service. I was relieved to find that I could book a return ticket, first class, all the way from Failsworth to London and back. I proudly showed it to Edith when I got back to Roman Road, but she was far from overjoyed; "I can't go all that way by myself, Davy, can't Arthur come with me?"

"No chuck, I don't have enough cash for another ticket, and besides, two people would draw more attention than one. I've booked you first class, so you'll be all right — no one will interfere with a posh young lady travelling first class."

"How will I know where to go with the jewellery?" Edith cried. I explained that an old friend of mine, a gent, had once given me an address in London that took valuables, no questions asked. This chap had used it a time or two, when he was stuck for the readies, having made some bad choices at the races, just as I had done myself. All she had to do was get a taxi at the station in London, go to the address, and then stay in a small hotel nearby — the taxi driver would know of one, as the jeweller would get plenty of business that required immediate attention. Edith was scared stiff, suggesting that I should go myself, or even Arthur, but I told her that it had to be her. I might be apprehended, because the police would have reported the incident to the brewery by now — a landlord couldn't just leave a pub unattended, and Arthur would like as not disappear with the money, if he managed to sell the jewellery. Two days later, I accompanied Edith to Manchester by train from Failsworth, and put her on the London express locomotive, a very long train with a huge engine. She'd dressed very modestly, in an outfit borrowed from Gertie, and had applied her make-up very carefully. "You mustn't look tarty," Arthur remarked, earning a filthy look from me! She had a first class return ticket in her purse, a little cash, and the jewellery, well concealed in a small suitcase borrowed, once again, from Gertie, and also containing another of the girl's outfits. Arthur and I both doubted whether we would ever see her again, but four days later we met her as planned at the station in Manchester. She was one of the first passengers off the train, and ran straight into my arms, obviously well pleased with herself. She told us, in between hugging us both, that she had managed to get a good price for the jewellery by flaunting her charms, and she clearly expected us to be over the moon. I had hoped that she would have acquired a much better price, as some of my mother's pieces were very fine indeed. However, drawing on my eternal optimism, I soon began to look on the bright side — anything was better than nothing, and I had also bought some time to look about for new employment. Charlie was greatly impressed by the amount that Edith had brought home, pointing out that he would have had to work at the coalface "a hell of a while" to earn that kind of money, but he point blank refused payment for our lodgings. "Nay lad," he told me. "You gave us all a damn good time every summer when we came over, and we're proud to be able to return the compliment. We've got the spare bedroom, now that young Charlie's married, so you can stay as long as you like, as long as Arthur doesn't mind kipping on the sofa. It's just a pity that we can't offer you next door, but the folk renting it have paid the next quarter in advance. I could ask them to look for other accommodation when that expires, and you could move in, rent free, until you're back on your feet again!"

I was truly touched by the Cookes' generosity, but said that there was no way that I would consider sponging off them, now that I had some cash. I would pay board and lodgings, until I could find my family a permanent home. "What kind of work will you be looking for?" Charlie enquired a few days later, "only I've been asking round, quietly mind, and I think I might be on to summat. You did a bit of undertaking in your younger days, if I'm not mistaken?"

"I did indeed, and quite enjoyed it. I certainly won't be looking for another pub!" Charlie and I had a good laugh, chatting about old escapades for a while, and then I asked Charlie what he had up his sleeve. "Well, our local undertaker died a couple of years ago, and his widow hasn't sold the business yet, as far as I can gather."

"Maybe it was on its last legs," I pointed out, but Charlie doubted that. "It must have made good money, lad. We have regular funerals in this neck of the woods, what with industrial accidents and the like. The widow still lives in the posh house next to the business — it might be worth an enquiry."

I was delighted, thinking that this was just the opening that I had been praying for, so I brushed down my suit, getting

Edith to press it with Annie's flat iron. I then made an appointment to visit the grieving widow, and went along at the agreed time, a spring once again in my step. Despite using all of my charm and powers of persuasion, however, I cut no ice with the old lady, who told me that the business was not for sale. I explained that I only wanted to buy the "goodwill" of the business, and would happily find another yard to set up my own premises, but she remained adamant. I visited on two or three further occasions, each time increasing my offer, but she refused all of my blandishments. The business was definitely not for sale! I couldn't help thinking that she probably believed that a relative of the poor Cooke family would never make a go of the business, and would be unable to find any asking price. I was disappointed, but kept my spirits up, travelling by bus and train all over the surrounding neighbourhood, looking for an opening. If only I could call on my wealthy friends in Newcastle for references, but of course that was out of the question. I would probably be arrested if my whereabouts ever came to light, and charged with defrauding the brewery. In the meantime, rather worryingly, the money was fast running out, and we couldn't sponge off Charlie and Annie for ever!

I arrived back at Charlie's, ready to tell him that we were moving on, once we had found a cheap place, to be greeted by the girls, Bessie, Gertie and Edith, all squealing with joy and proudly holding up a wee kitten. "Where's the old mouser?" I asked, and Annie appeared from the kitchen, laughing. "Oh, old Tabby has finally passed away. God knows how old she was, but we've got a new kitten from one of the neighbours, and guess what we're going to call her, David!"

"Guess, guess!" the girls shrieked, and I couldn't believe that they were getting so excited about a new moggy, so I shrugged my shoulders and said, "I give up, please tell me!"

"Why, Tishy, of course, to remind you of what happens to you when you put all your eggs in one basket!" Despite myself, I couldn't help laughing, saying that the wee thing would probably have done better in the big race than her namesake! Charlie came in, black as coal, wondering what was so funny. I felt my worries slipping away, and after a good dinner, told Charlie that we were moving on, thanking him and Annie for all the help they'd given us. "I don't know what we would have done without you folks, but it's time we stood on our own feet again. God bless you both!"

"Where will you go?" Charlie enquired, and I said anywhere there was work for joiners. "We won't need much in the way of accommodation, and there's only the three of us. A couple of rooms will do, until I find a decent job and Edith and Arthur can try to find part-time work." Charlie probably wondered why Arthur couldn't get a proper job, but said nothing. His own son, Charlie junior, couldn't hold down a job since he'd come back from the war, and his new wife was the breadwinner in that little family! A couple of days later, he took me aside after supper, and told me of rental accommodation he'd heard of in Moston, near his pit. Some of his mates lived near the pit, and knew of cheap rooms nearby, not up to much, they said, but they'd do for a bit. I walked over to Moston early one morning, with Charlie pushing his bike, and saw the buildings with rooms to rent — pretty similar slum properties to the places folk lived in near The Vine in Newcastle. I checked the information on the board outside one of the properties, and Charlie pointed over to an office, where folk could enquire about rents and such like. "You get to work, Charlie, and I'll see what's what!" I waved him off, and with a heavy heart, waited outside the office until it was due to open at nine o'clock. The "Janitor," as he called himself, arrived half an hour later, and without apology opened up the end building, which had several vacant "properties", as he euphemistically called them. "No kids, no pets, and rent on the first day of every month, one month in advance." I looked around and settled for a ground floor, one bedroom property. It was dark and dingy, but at least it had its own door onto the street, no rickety stairs to climb, and no other tenants to contend with on the stairs. I paid the first month's rent, with a little extra for the janitor. No harm in oiling the wheels, I told myself, and was rewarded by the man offering to get a woman in to clean the place up for a couple of bob. The windows were thick with grime, and the whole place smelt decidedly musty, but beggars can't be choosers! I walked back alone with a sinking feeling in the pit of my stomach — how had things come to this? What would Edith and Arthur say when they saw their new home? I was pleasantly surprised at Edith's reaction, when she learned that I had taken a property for the three of us in Moston. "Oh, great," she exclaimed, "that's where our Wilf lives!" I had heard a few references to Wilf Bellingham from other members of his family. Apparently, he was a hopeless drunk, even by their standards, and had moved away from Newcastle a few years earlier, his wife throwing him out in despair. Edith had an address for him in her "Memory Book", as she called it, and wrote a letter to him straight away, telling him that they were to be neighbours, but not to tell the rest of the family, as they would be after her husband's blood. A few days later, a letter arrived for Edith, beautifully written, to my surprise, inviting us all over to his place at the weekend. With nothing better to do, I told her to reply in the affirmative, saying that we'd take a few beers with us. "Oh no," Edith laughed, "he's a reformed character, and is teetotal now. I'll make us all a cup of tea!" We went to Moston by bus, Charlie telling us where to catch it, and I got a further surprise on meeting Wilf; he was a handsome man, well dressed and sober as a judge! I asked him where he worked, as he clearly could not have afforded his pleasant flat if he was on the dole, and he told me that he was employed by a large engineering firm in Droylsden, Ferguson Pailin by name. He was an engineer by profession, with full accreditation by his professional body. "Fergie's," as he called the firm, manufactured railway engines, and on hearing that Arthur was unemployed, offered to get him an apprenticeship there, if he wanted one. "I want to be a professional snooker player," Arthur replied, "but Dad wouldn't let me bring my cue when we ran off!" Edith had clearly told him of our narrow escape from The Vine, and he laughed, and told us that he used to play a bit of snooker in his younger days, and that he would look out his old cue. While he was out of the room, Edith said that her brother had been a very good player before he took to drink, so his cue ought to be pretty good. It was very good, according to Arthur, who knew a thing or two about cues, and we all got on like a house on fire, drinking tea and eating sticky buns, provided by our charming host. Arthur was so elated by the prospect of playing snooker again, with a better cue than any he'd ever owned, that he agreed to start an apprenticeship at the factory, if Wilf could get him one. "Good lad," Wilf replied, and the two of them shook hands on it over another cup of tea! "What are you thinking of doing, David?" he asked, and I hedged, saying that I'd not yet settled on anything, but was a joiner by trade. "I don't think I can help you much there," Wilf said. "We only have a few joiners, and they don't get much money."

"He talks as if he owns the place," I complained to Edith, once we were in bed in Charlie's spare room later. "I know," she laughed, "his firm are very good to him, very understanding about his problem; you see, David, he falls off the wagon from time to time, but apparently he's a brilliant engineer, and saves them a lot of money when he's sober, so they put up with his absences. It's a pity that his wife couldn't!"

The removal day arrived, and I hired a van to move what little stuff we had. As it was a Saturday, Charlie and Annie were able to help, also giving us some pots and pans, which Annie insisted were surplus to requirements. She had made curtains for our windows, and Charlie stayed over, sleeping on a camp bed, which Annie had "found in the attic." I to-ed and fro-ed in the van, and collected a cheap "lot" of furniture from a junk shop, and when everything was installed, the place looked almost habitable. The following week, Arthur and I gave the rooms a coat of paint, and Edith found a second-hand rug going cheap at a local shop. Wilf came over at the weekend and congratulated us on our new home. "You've certainly bucked the place up," he laughed, as we drank tea and sampled a delicious sponge cake that he'd brought with him. "I've fixed up an apprenticeship for you, lad," he informed Arthur. "You're to go along for an interview on Tuesday, but it's just a formality. You're to be taken on as an apprentice welder. It's not much money, but you'll be guaranteed a job at the end of it. Welders are well paid at our place because good welders are hard to come by." Arthur thanked him, probably reckoning that it would have to do until he could make a living at snooker. Thankfully, he didn't say as much to Wilf.

Charlie and Annie went over to Aggie's the following weekend and brought Grandma and Grandad to Failsworth on the tram. "Why didn't you tell us?" I exclaimed, "Arthur and I could have helped!"

"I know," Charlie replied, "but you're only just getting over all your upheaval. We managed fine, and the old folk seem contented with Charlie junior's old room. We'll bring all their bits and pieces another time," I told Edith, who in turn told Wilf, so the following Sunday, Wilf and I drove over to Aggie's in Wilf's car, and brought back the rest of their few possessions. Annie had roast beef with all the trimmings waiting for us when we arrived at Roman Road, and Wilf laughed, asking if he could help every weekend in the future!

Edith got a job skivvying for a family of five kids, whose dad was doing well in some business or other, which was never specified, and I kept my eyes and ears open, taking anything that came along, no matter how menial. I found that I was in demand for my joinery skills, once they became known, Wilf spreading the word in the local hostelries, which he had begun to frequent once again, much to Edith's dismay!

CHAPTER 11
HARD TIMES

All was going pretty well, considering, until Edith became pregnant, an accident we could well have done without. "Oh God, David, we'll be evicted, the Jannie said no kids, didn't he?"

"I'll speak to him, love," I replied, and when I returned, I explained to Edith that all was well. The man was happy to waive the rules, as we were good tenants, quiet, clean, and paid the rent on the dot. He'd laughed and told me that there weren't too many folk around here like that, and patted me on the back, wishing the family well. It probably helped that a bottle of whisky changed hands as I was leaving the office!

The pregnancy got off to a bad start, with Edith suffering violent bouts of morning sickness, resulting in her losing her job. She also developed a persistent cough, brought on by the dampness in the flat, and this eventually turned into bronchitis. I insisted that she went to the local doctor's surgery, and he stated the obvious, saying that the only real cure would be to find a better place to live, but failing that, she had to rest as much as possible, and take a tablespoon of the cough linctus that he prescribed, whenever necessary.

I could see that Arthur was becoming increasingly bored by his apprenticeship, and he skived off whenever he could, preferring to help Edith during the day by doing the shopping and washing, and trying his luck in the local billiard halls at night. He had some success, making a bit of money, which kept him in cigarettes, with a little over to give Edith for his keep. It soon became increasingly difficult to win money playing snooker however, for as he became known as a player to watch, the other guys were loath to give him a game, and he had to keep going further afield to avoid being recognised. He told me that he felt that he was losing his edge too, due to lack of practice. If only we could have stayed in Newcastle, where he could have practised all day at the club, and probably turned professional, as Joe Davis had suggested to him on that famous night. The crunch came one night, when he returned home in the small hours to find me sat in an armchair, obviously waiting for him. He must have thought that he would cop for a black eye, but instead I told him, "Sit down, son, it's time we had a chat." Arthur replied that he'd better get to bed, having to be up early for work, but I just smiled at him and said, "Getting up early for work is no problem, son. I developed a system when I was an apprentice in the Undertakers in Newcastle."

"Oh, yes?" replied Arthur, sitting down and probably beginning to smell a rat. "Yes son, I would come home in the small hours, just like you, get undressed, first setting my alarm clock for the usual time, and then get into bed. When the alarm went off, even if it was only half an hour later, I'd get up, wash, dress and trot off to work, so that I could clock in on time — that way, nobody knew that I'd been out on the "razz" and could report me to my mother." My jovial tone must have confused him, as he replied that nobody living nearby knew where he worked, and so couldn't report him, and anyway, he could usually make more money in the clubs than he could at

Fergie Pailin's. "Usually perhaps, but not on a regular basis, and its regularity that we need here, son, so take my advice for once — clock in on time, five mornings a week, collect your pay packet on Friday afternoons, and hand it over, unopened to Edith at six o'clock when you get home. She'll probably give you a shilling or two for yourself, as she's got a soft spot for you, though God knows why!"

"And if I don't?" Arthur replied, throwing caution to the winds. "And if you don't, Edith will tell me when I get home from work, and when you saunter through that door in the middle of the night, I'll be waiting for you, and I'll knock the living daylights out of you! At that point, you'll collect your things, including that precious cue of yours, and bugger off! We can't carry passengers any more. I'll say good night now son, as I, like you, have to be up early in the morning for work." I went off to bed and left Arthur to assess his options. He had nowhere else to live, and no other job to go to. His winnings varied considerably, and he was becoming too well known in all the clubs, so much so that other chaps were declining when he suggested a little flutter, "to make the game more interesting!" He'd told me that he'd had to leave a few of his haunts in a hurry, and would soon have to travel much further afield to find suitable opponents. With no home, no regular income, no winnings, and no prospects, he would soon be in dire straits. He must have pondered this for what was left of the night, lying on the sofa that served as his bed, and then, future decided, he washed his face and set off to work, Edith handing him his lunch box as she always did. From that day on, he only played snooker occasionally at the weekend, and handed over his pay packet, unopened as instructed. He seemed to sense that I was pleased with his decision, and slowly, but surely, our relationship improved.

It was a couple of years later that Arthur found out that it had been Edith who had blown the whistle on his timekeeping, as she couldn't manage when his pay had been docked. She'd asked Wilf to check up on his hours, and had decided to take action, telling me to go easy on him, as he was a good lad really, helping her out a lot in the house when she felt too exhausted with coughing to do much herself. She was, of course, also getting bigger and heavier by the day, as her pregnancy wore on.

Wilf told Arthur about this incident, also telling him that he'd changed his ways in the nick of time, as the firm was just about to cancel his apprenticeship. It must have felt strange to Arthur that they would sack him for his poor timekeeping, and frequent absences, yet they would keep Wilf on, when they never knew when he would go AWOL. The difference was that Wilf made a lot of money for the company when he was sober, and Arthur was just an apprentice. Wilf's behaviour, however, was becoming more and more erratic, and Arthur told me that he could usually smell drink on him when they met. Edith confided in us that she was becoming desperately worried about her brother, but didn't know what to do. She'd spoken to his pal at the Alcoholics Anonymous, and he'd told her that things would come to a head soon, if Wilf couldn't get a grip! "He has such a good brain, but it's becoming more and more pickled!" he had told her.

The next time he came over, however, he was sober, and had apparently "pulled himself together," as Edith put it. He looked gaunt, and not his old handsome self, and he was very subdued, but he was sober! "His health will improve, now he's eating again," Edith assured us, "Thank God for the AA!"

The next couple of years were difficult times for the Brindley and Cooke families. I was only able to get odd jobs, so my income varied a great deal. A teetotal Wilf no longer frequented the pubs, so he couldn't drum up any business for me anymore; "Thank God!" as Edith often said. To top it all, she had three babies in quick succession, Betty, Marjorie and Roy. She was still often incapacitated by her bronchitis, but somehow managed to keep her sense of humour! Some well-wishers brought bunches of flowers after the births, which made her cough all the more, and she often said that she'd have preferred a Guinness! In later life, she used to joke that she didn't want flowers on her coffin, "just a crate of Blue Bass!" Wilf came round to see her quite often, and depending on whether he was on or off the wagon, they would have a cup of tea, or a Guinness, quite a few in fact, if Wilf was backsliding again. Edith never preached sobriety to him, partly because she liked a drink herself, but mainly because she knew it wouldn't do any good. "Preaching just annoys him, and makes him worse," was her view. They would have a laugh together, whatever condition he was in, though neither of them had much to laugh about. Wilf's divorce had come through, and his ex-wife had remarried, and had since had a baby, which seemed to upset him greatly. Edith told me that her sister-in-law had always wanted a family, but Wilf had been unable to provide her with one, and this had been the real reason for their separation. Apparently, his drinking wasn't that bad, up until then! Even his employer was losing patience with him, never knowing whether he would turn up for work or not, his behaviour becoming more and more unpredictable. He told Arthur that he felt that his only friend in the whole world was Edith. Arthur, meantime, had stuck to his apprenticeship, and became a fully-fledged and very competent welder. Wilf always told him what a grand lad he was. "Your father doesn't appreciate you, son," he'd say. "He doesn't realise how lucky he is!" Arthur increasingly enjoyed going to Uncle Charlie's at the weekends, where he was very well fed by Auntie Annie, and he got on well with his cousin, Charlie junior, when he came round to visit his parents. Charlie junior was still "in the doldrums", as everyone put it, and his wife, Emily, seldom came with him. "She gets fed up with me and my troubles," he said, "and who can blame her?" Gertie's shop was doing well though, and she had become friendly with a local businessman, giving rise to a lot of gossip, which the Cookes ignored. As Charlie senior said, "Folk will always make mountains out of molehills." Arthur himself still fancied Bessie, the youngest of the Cooke clan, but of course she was his cousin, and he felt that such a relationship would be frowned upon, and he certainly didn't want to upset her family.

Wilf's downward slide continued, and Fergie's told him that as things stood, they couldn't continue to employ him; he could either pull himself together, or look for another job. "Who the hell would take me on?" he had asked, when we were all having a beer together, waiting for Edith to bring the kids home from a birthday party that they had attended down the street. "Fergie's won't sack you, Wilf," Arthur told him. "You've pulled yourself together before, and you'll do it again!"

"Aye lad, but that was when I wanted to, now I don't give a damn!" Edith and the kids came in, and our conversation was interrupted, as the excited youngsters showed off their goodies from the party.

The terrible end for Wilf came sooner than anyone expected, especially Edith. His mangled body was found on a railway line, along which he had been walking home after yet another night's drinking, out to the world as usual. He could only be identified by his signet ring, given to him by his wife on their wedding day. The engine driver had seen him on the track ahead but hadn't been able to stop the train in time. The poor fellow was traumatised, and never drove a train again! Edith always said that her beloved brother had committed suicide, whilst walking on a railway track dead drunk, and that seemed to sum it up. Edith told me that she was going to let her family know about Wilf's sad demise, and also invite them to the funeral, and despite my obvious misgivings, I managed not to air them. I felt that I had caused my wife enough problems and didn't want to add to them. If the worst came to the worst, I'd get beaten up or arrested, and I faced that prospect with all the dignity I could muster.

The day of the interment dawned bright and sunny, but still Edith had received no reply to her letter. Arthur, Edith and I walked sombrely to the local church, dressed in black, or as near as we could manage. Charlie and Annie were waiting in the porch, and we all went in together. A group of men were seated apart from the rest of the mourners at the back of the church, and there were very few other attendees, just a couple of bosses from Ferguson Pailin, and Wilf's mentor friend from the AA, who had so accurately seen into Wilf's future. After the brief service, we all walked slowly out to the graveyard, where the group of men, five in all, stood together, well away from the grave. Once Wilf had been laid to rest, they left without a word to their sister, or anyone else for that matter. Clearly, she and I had never been forgiven for the Cesarewitch disaster, and that was the last Edith ever saw of her family. She wept copiously when we got back to the flat, and whether she cried for her Wilf, or for her other lost brothers and sisters, we never found out.

Chapter 12
A Bit of Luck at Last

As I often said, things could only get better, and sure enough the tide turned soon after, when luckily, I spotted an advert in a local paper for a joiner's job at Belle Vue, the Manchester Zoological Gardens. I went along with hundreds of others and managed to secure a second interview. Edith pressed my best suit, the only one I had left that wasn't threadbare, and sent me off looking more like a manager than an interviewee for menial work. She looked out my homburg hat, which I'd always worn at race meetings, and had brought with me when we made our escape from The Vine. Brushing it well, she popped it on my head as I was leaving. "It'll bring you luck!" she called after me, "That and your pixie, for that matter!" Something certainly did, as I got the job, although I think that my joiner's certification helped more than the hat, or the pixie! I learned later that it was none of these things that had done the trick. The interviewing panel were more impressed by my size, as I towered over the other hopefuls!

The Zoological Gardens had been having a lot of trouble with vandals and disgruntled workers, the former smashing up the rides in the funfair, and the latter springing lightning strikes in their campaign for higher wages. The park management suspected that the vandals and the strikers were one and the same, in other words, the workforce, on whom the gardens depended. The zoo had been losing money for a while; local people were no longer excited by the sight of wild animals in cages, but looking for other thrills on which to spend their hard-earned cash. The labour troubles and falling visitor numbers had taken their toll on the foreman joiner, who had suffered a nervous breakdown. The interviewing panel decided to try me out, hoping that my size might calm things down at the funfair, which they desperately needed to start making money. My starting salary was certainly nothing to write home about, but at least it was regular, and I went off to work every morning with a spring in my step again. The other joiners were told that I was on trial for the foreman's job, and therefore tried it on a bit at first, but my size and manner quickly dampened their courage, and I soon impressed the management, even talking them into giving the men a small pay rise. It actually cost them nothing at all, as I had already sacked three of the malcontents. Thus, I became popular with my men, and my trial period ended in success; I was promoted to foreman joiner after only six months, and received a good pay rise myself. Things were beginning to look up at last, and Edith, Arthur and I went out for a drink that weekend to celebrate our good fortune, our first real bit of luck since the disaster at The Vine. As I was now in permanent employment, we qualified for a council house in the Manchester area, and moved in a couple of months later, Charlie and Annie helping us with the removal. Edith organised a house-warming party to celebrate the "turning of the tide," and all of the Cookes attended. Bessie looked splendid, in Arthur's opinion at least, wearing a green dress that complimented her mop of auburn hair; not for the first time, I'm sure he wished that she wasn't his cousin!

Belle Vue was an eye-opener for all the family; it covered a vast area of Manchester, and although it had opened as a small zoo, it had flourished and extended over the years.

Gradually, though, the zoo had become the least profitable of the Gardens' features. It was still a draw however, folk delighting at the sight of the exotic animals, lions, tigers, elephants and the like, pacing up and down in their cages. This popularity had resulted in the establishment of a circus every Christmas, with clowns, acrobats and performing animals. Children were well catered for with donkey rides, and subsequently, elephant and camel rides as well. Manchester was expanding as the North's biggest engineering and manufacturing centre, and Belle Vue had grown with it, taking full advantage of the fact that working people now had more money in their pockets to spend on entertainment. Naturally, there were many exotic bars for the grown-ups, with play areas outside, where the kids were supervised by nice ladies in fabulous costumes. The fairground had also developed, and it was for the purpose of improving this enterprise that I had been taken on.

The 'go-ahead' management wanted something spectacular to bring in more punters to the aforementioned fairground, and so announced their intention to fund a majestic roller coaster ride, which would astound folk of all ages. Thus, "the Bobs", as it became known, was commissioned, and my team of joiners and I contemplated the complex and somewhat terrifying job of building the carriages and the track. I studied the plans and dimensions of the ride, and more in hope than expectation, told my men that they were the finest at their trade in the world, and that they would come in for some fantastic bonuses as the construction developed. I pointed out to the bosses that a few aspects of the ride, such as the height of some of the sections, the gradients of the downward slopes, and the sharp turns at several of the corners, were well-nigh impossible to build, but I could find a way round these problems, as long as the men were suitably motivated. Many hours of overtime would be required, at double pay, with extra financial incentives offered once sections were completed. I had already impressed my employers with my expertise at solving maintenance issues, so they agreed, "as long as the men don't make impossible demands!"

"Remember," I said calmly, "these men will be building a totally new-fangled construction, which must be safe, at all costs — just one accident could close Belle Vue down altogether, with compensation claims running into millions, and folk fearing to go on any of the rides."

"Go ahead then, David," came the reply. "In for a penny, in for a pound!"

The work eventually got underway, and I was forced to pour over the drawings every evening at home, often into the small hours, making modifications where necessary. "The bugger who designed this couldn't build a sandcastle," I told Edith, who probably wished by then that I had never applied for the job at Belle Vue after all, as it would probably be the death of me!

The Cookes' visits gradually fell away, as I had no time for socialising, or for anything else, for that matter. I think that Arthur then began to realise what had made me so successful at running the pubs. I gave every venture my all, letting no obstacle stand in my way, and he told me that he could see that now. He also reminded me that I could, however, throw caution to the wind when the challenge became too great, as with the "Tishy" debacle. He sometimes found himself praying that all would go well this time, and that his old man would manage to pull something out of the hat!

Early on in the construction process, a tragedy occurred, when one of the joiners fell from a high stretch of the track, breaking his back. I fought the bosses long and hard for adequate compensation for the poor bloke, although his blood count had shown that he had drunk alcohol the night before the accident. "Only a couple of pints," I pointed out, knowing myself that I drank at least that amount every night as I pored over the plans. "The poor lad will never work again, and what effect will that have on the rest of the men? They're the best in the business, and will be irreplaceable if they walk out en masse! What will become of your investment in the roller coaster then, and in Belle Vue, for that matter, for if you get a slating in the press, a lot of custom will disappear, folk thinking that nothing here is safe, all built for cheapness?" I finally won the day, the bosses paying out more than adequately, thus getting some free good publicity for the ride, with the injured man thanking them publicly for their concern for their employees' welfare, and the safety of the public as well. Arthur and I went out for a pint to celebrate that night, and he congratulated me on my victory, saying that I could always be relied upon to pull the fat out of the fire. "Not always, son, as you well know. Have another half on me, and then we'll call it a night." We walked home, and I felt closer to my son than I had ever done before, wishing that we had been buddies when he was growing up. Ah well, I thought to myself, it's never too late!

"The Bobs" was eventually completed, and passed a safety inspection carried out by the council's inspectorate. No more serious accidents had occurred, only the occasional joiner breaking a thumb, or falling off a gantry, resulting in a broken ankle — nothing more serious, thank God!

Chapter 13
Happy Days are Here Again

The Grand Opening was organised by management, with several local brass bands engaged. Bunting was festooned on every available surface, and free refreshments provided for all; smoked salmon and caviar for the councillors and invited guests, and sandwiches for the general public, with lorry loads of sweets for the kids. Free beer was also provided for the masses, with lemonade for the kids, and the invited guests and councillors drank wine or whisky, whichever was their preference. The charge for the ride was one shilling, a "bob" in local parlance, and the name stuck. Forever after, the roller coaster was affectionately known as "The Bobs." This charge was waived for the opening day, and the event received massive publicity in the local press, thus guaranteeing an enormous crowd. Many of these people were so far away from the ride that they had to climb up onto stalls or other rides, in order to see what was going on. Waiters and waitresses rushed round, trying to ensure that everyone received their fair share of the free refreshments.

The inaugural ride was scheduled to take place at three p.m., but was twenty-five minutes late, as the management, councillors and invited guests couldn't get through the throng to embark, and sections of the crowd who couldn't see what was going on became alarmed, the rumour going round that something serious had happened, making the ride unsafe. The whole purpose of the inaugural ride was to demonstrate that the ride was indeed safe, so I climbed aboard myself, into the very last carriage, watched by Edith and Arthur, both of whom had their fingers firmly crossed. The invited guests began to look less than confident, as they struggled through the crowds to climb aboard the carriages, and an ominous hush spread through the spectators. It was just before the carriages began to slowly roll along that I decided to do something totally unrehearsed. I lit my pipe, and sat back in my seat, surveying the milling throng, many of whom gasped at my audacity. I secretly prayed that this act of bravado wouldn't turn out to be my last, but I needn't have worried. In company with the screams of the guests on the ride, and the crowds watching the carriages hurtling round, up and down the death-defying inclines, I puffed away, completely at ease. Job done, I thought! The guests finally stepped shakily off "The Experience", as it had been dubbed, to the cheers of the crowds and the press, and so the first customers then boarded. I remained casually in my seat, "taking a break," as I told the press later. I stayed aboard for the first four trips before disembarking, attempting to make my way through the crowds. "I've overstayed my welcome," I laughingly told them, "I'll be getting my marching orders if you don't let me through quick!" My picture appeared in all of the daily papers the following morning, and I was a celebrity overnight! The management were delighted by my act of bravado, and gave me a substantial bonus for getting the job safely completed, and proving to the public that the ride was indeed safe. I thanked them, but also told them that had I had little or no confidence in the safety of the structure, I'd have made my thoughts very clear to the designer of the ride, and to them, adding that if I hadn't modified the plans in several key areas, God knows what would have happened!

I regularly took my tea breaks on "the Bobs," and Arthur would often join me on a Saturday afternoon, when he wanted a word with me. It was on one of these occasions that he told me that he had proposed to Bessie Cooke, and that she had accepted, much to his amazement. "Why are you surprised, lad?" I asked, and he said that surely it was obvious — she was Uncle Charlie's daughter, and therefore they were first cousins. "Do you think that we're doing the right thing, Dad?" he asked me. "It's always been good enough for royalty, son, so I reckon it's good enough for you!" I replied. "Pop round and tell Edith, she'll no doubt throw you a party!" She duly did — Edith was always one for a party — and a good time was had by all, not a single person bothered in the slightest by the happy couple's close relations. Arthur told me that he often thought ruefully of the wasted years, but "better late than never!" was Bessie's view on the matter. "I'd just about given you up," she laughed, echoing Edith's words when I had proposed to her a few years earlier.

"The Bobs" was a great success, folk coming to Belle Vue from all over the North, and even further afield, to experience the thrills and sheer terror that the ride evoked. I was cheered by the crowds whenever I climbed aboard for my break, and my pay and standing with the management both went up in leaps and bounds.

It was partly due to this triumph that I was then offered the exciting job of commentating on the speedway. "I've never commentated in my life," I laughed, "or even watched any motorbike racing, for that matter!"

"It's very good money, David," said one of the bosses. "You're a genuine star at this place now, and folk want to see and hear more of you; read a few of the speedway magazines in the back office and let us know what you think." I decided that commentating on this daft sport — motorbikes tearing round and round a track — would be child's play, "money for jam," and after talking it over with Edith, I accepted for two evenings per week. I couldn't understand how I'd become so well-known almost overnight, but Edith assured me that it was because I was a fine-looking fellow, who could also pull in the crowds. The management gave me the money to buy an evening suit, and off I went for my first night, revelling in the big build-up that I was given by some fellow with a microphone — "David Brindley, the man who brought "the Bobs" to Manchester, totally unafraid of the highs and lows, the twists and turns of this monstrous ride, and now ready to bring that courage to the speedway. Our team will have no trouble crushing the opposition now that David is behind us!" He was eventually drowned out by the cheers of the crowd, mostly Belle Vue's home supporters, and handed the mic over to me. I thanked everyone for the lovely welcome, and waved my lucky pixie on high, shouting that, with the help of my mascot and the cheers of the crowd, "Victory will be ours!" Fortunately, the team had a run of good luck that season, and came top of the league, a first for them, so my popularity increased even more, as did the family's income. Arthur had moved out to share a cottage with two mates from "Fergie's," in a little place called Woodhouses. It was easy cycling distance from there to his work, and no distance at all from Failsworth, so he could see more of the Cookes, especially the lovely Bessie, who was now his fiancée.

Following my success at the speedway, I was offered the job of commentating at the boxing on a Saturday night. This was much more to my taste than the speedway; I'd always enjoyed boxing, even when I was a young apprentice joiner, and had gone to many local bouts with my brother Isaac, who used to place bets for us, giving me a cut of the winnings if our man prevailed. I consulted Edith, who was simply delighted with yet another jump in our finances. She decided there and then that Friday would be our night for a bit of fun, with Tuesdays and Thursdays set aside for speedway, and Saturdays for the boxing. "What about the kids?" I enquired, as by this time we had three little ones. "Oh, Granny Malone from across the road can pop in and watch them for us. She loves the children, and the money we give her will cover a wee bottle of gin — she does like a drop from time to time! Arthur might help out as well; it's time he started paying us back a bit, after all we've done for him!"

"Messed up his snooker ambitions." I thought ruefully, but I knew that Edith deserved a break, after all she'd done for me. The arrangement was made with Granny Malone, and the pattern was set, Edith and I having our first night out in a long while, just like old times. When she reckoned that I'd had enough, Edith would take my arm and walk me home, more often than not to find the kids still up in their nighties, and Granny fast asleep by the remains of the fire, a contented smile on her old face, and an empty glass in her hand. "One night we'll come home to find the house burned to the ground, Granny and the kids along with it," I said to Edith one Friday night, after I'd drunk rather less than usual. This had been worrying me for a while, leaving the children in the care of the old girl, and so it was decided that Arthur should be called upon to assist. "After all, he can bring Bessie round as well, if he likes," Edith suggested, "and she can practise getting the kids ready for bed. Are they ever going to tie the knot, by the way? They'll be in their nineties by the time they get married, if they don't get a move on!" I offered that I thought they were saving up. "God knows why, they could live in the house next to the shop, and pay rent to Charlie and Annie."

"What they do is up to them, love," I replied, and the matter was closed. The next time I saw Arthur, I brought up the subject of babysitting, to give Bessie some training, as it were. "I don't think Bessie wants kids, perhaps because of the "cousins" thing, but I'll ask her to do the Friday nights with me, Dad." And so it was, that Arthur and Bessie came round every Friday evening after work, bringing with them fish and chips for all of us, and Granny Malone was discreetly pensioned off. As before, the kids were still all out of bed when we rolled in, but at least they were clean and ready for bed, the fire still blazing away. Bessie read them bedtime stories, and Arthur made a good job of washing the dishes, tidying up and keeping the fire going. "Bessie will make a good mother," I commented to Arthur. "Give over, Dad. You're just after some grandchildren!"

"Well, you're my only hope on that front — I'll be dead by the time these kids are grown up, and God only knows what Sally will produce, the only heirs being most likely 'airs' and graces!"

I had received an invitation to Sally's wedding in 1927, down in the London area, but I had declined, citing work commitments. Sally had sent a postcard from London a couple of months later, saying that Randles' parents hadn't turned up either. The only people at the ceremony had been RAF friends, but everything had gone well, and they were very happy. "At least she got her man in the end," was my only comment to Edith.

My fame spread quickly all over the North of England, what with my triumph at the opening day of "the Bobs", followed by my panache as commentator at the speedway, and at the boxing bouts on the Saturday nights. I found that I had a real talent for getting the crowd going at both venues, and loved walking on in all my finery, to the cheers of the blokes, and to the admiring glances from the ladies.

I had always taken the *Newcastle Gazette*, since our flight from The Vine, and when folk asked me why, I always said that I enjoyed reading about my old haunts, but Arthur later discovered that I secretly had another reason. On visiting Belle Vue one Saturday afternoon, he was told that I had taken a couple of days off, to attend my brother's funeral. I had seen Isaac's obituary in the paper, and this had given the time and place of the service. When I returned, I told Arthur that I'd spoken to Helen, Isaac's widow, and had told her that the biggest regret in my life had been my estrangement from my brother. I had always wanted to see him again, to make amends for our bitter disagreement. Helen had smiled, telling me that Isaac had also regretted this; he had wanted to get in touch, but had been too proud to make the first move, and now it was too late. "I think that you were both very much alike in character, a little stubborn and self-righteous, as Isaac told me your mother was. He said that you were chips off the same block, but he loved you, David, as you loved him. I'm so glad that you came today, please do come to the reception at our home." I had reluctantly declined, saying that I had to catch my train, but I was so relieved that I'd gone to the funeral. I felt now that

Isaac and I had made our peace, at last.

I was soon approached by several drinks firms, offering me good money to advertise their products, and as I told Edith, I liked a drink as she well knew, so to get paid for having a pint, or downing a bottle, was manna from Heaven! The high point of my modelling career was a Guinness advert that adorned the billboards all over Lancashire, with me holding the bottle to the fore, wearing my joiner's leather apron, and a wicked twinkle in my eye. I continued working at Belle Vue until my sixty-seventh birthday, using my various talents to provide a good income for my family, who had now grown up into two bonnie young women, Betty and Marjorie, and my son, Roy, who was the apple of my eye. Roy was called up in 1944, or conscripted, as was the official term. He was moved around a lot with his unit, but wrote home regularly, on Edith's express instruction. The Potsdam Agreement was signed in August 1945, with photos of Winston Churchill, Franklin D Roosevelt and Joseph Stalin in all the papers — the war was over, thank God! A couple of days later, Edith received a belated letter from Roy, saying that the war would be over in a few days, and that he would be coming home. "Get the bunting out, Mum," were his words, and we were all overjoyed. Roy was safe, and would soon be coming home. Edith began making preparations for the homecoming at once, though she knew that it could be weeks, or even months before he walked up the garden path. Imagine our shock, however, when we received a telegram from the War Office a few days after his last letter, informing us that our son Roy had been killed, four days after the war had ended. The truck that he and others from his unit had been travelling in had been blown up by a landmine, and very few of the men had survived. I had retired only a couple of months earlier at the age of sixty-seven, Belle Vue giving me a great send-off, and I'd been making plans for fishing expeditions, and trips to the races, that myself and Roy would enjoy together. I was devastated, and couldn't cope with my wife's and daughters' grief; "all the weeping and wailing," as I called it. The following Saturday lunchtime, I knocked on Arthur and Bessie's front door in Failsworth, and Arthur opened it to see me standing there, ashen faced, on the step.

"Come in, Dad," he said, "You look shattered!" At this I began to sob uncontrollably, my whole body shaking. "What's wrong, Dad?" Poor Arthur didn't know what to say or do, but eventually I managed to tell him of Roy's tragic death. Arthur had heard that Roy was safe, and would soon be home, so he was as shocked as I was. "How did you get here, Dad?" he asked, and I slowly managed to get a grip, telling him that I'd walked over from Gorton, ten miles away. At this point little Margaret, Bessie and Arthur's nine-year-old daughter, came into the room, excited by the unexpected visit, asking what Grandad had brought for her. Bessie followed, and Arthur asked that she take the child out and bring in a couple of bottles of beer. We sat drinking for a while, saying little, and a while later, Bessie brought in sandwiches and a half bottle of whisky. A couple of hours later, I announced that I was ready to set off back home, and Arthur said that he would accompany me, but it would be better if we went on the bus. "Nay, lad," I told him, "I need the walk. I'll be all right when I get home, there's nothing like fresh air and exercise to lift the spirits!" I left without another word, hearing later that Arthur had got a right rollicking for letting me go. They were informed the next day, however, that I had made it home safely, and had begun the unenviable task of calming the family down. "At least Roy would have felt nothing," I said to them, "and he didn't come home severely wounded or destroyed in his mind, like young Charlie. There's always a bright side!"

CHAPTER 14
RECONCILIATION

David passed away in 1958, aged eighty, after a debilitating illness, and all of his family attended his funeral. His best friend, Charlie and his wife, Annie had already died, but his beloved Sally came, staying in Failsworth with Arthur and Bessie, and so brother and sister became reconciled, visiting each other regularly for the rest of their lives.

The funeral was very well attended, the bosses at Belle Vue all present, even though David had retired thirteen years earlier. His obituary in the Manchester papers ended with the words "In every way, David Brindley was a big man!"

Edith had written to Helen, Isaac's widow, inviting her to the funeral. She received a reply from John, Isaac's and Helen's son, saying that his mother was now in a nursing home and very frail, but he would like to come in her place. He made a point of speaking to Sally and Arthur at the reception later, saying that their respective fathers would now be up there in the Great beyond, still arguing over the rights and wrongs of their dispute, but happy at last to be together again.

"Amen to that!"